*BLOWOUT AT
PLATFORM A*

Blowout at Platform A

~~~~~~~~~~

The Crisis that

Awakened a Nation

LEE DYE

Doubleday & Company, Inc.

1971   GARDEN CITY, NEW YORK

For my Father,
Harold E. Dye

ACKNOWLEDGMENTS

It is traditional for an author to give credit to his spouse for such wifely virtues as patience and understanding during the absorbing process of writing a book. In this case, such credit would be grossly inadequate. When this book was only about two thirds completed, and with a deadline less than a month away, I had the untimely gall to fall off my roof and break my left arm in several places. My wife, Sherie, who had been serving as chief typist and literary critic, took on the added chores of dictation. She earned credit at least equal to mine for the authorship of this book.

And to my two daughters, Trina and Katherine, and to their many little friends who wondered from time to time how such sweet little girls could put up with such a grouch of a father, I can only ask for forgiveness. Someday, perhaps, it will make more sense.

In addition, there are a number of authors to whom I am greatly indebted.

The oil industry is as complex as it is huge. Had it not been for the writings of other authors I would still be trying to piece together the confusing past and present of the international oil industry. Many books were useless, because they were obviously underwritten by the industry, and their contents were thus subject to suspicion.

By contrast, Christopher Tugendhat's book, *Oil: the Biggest Business,* (G. P. Putnam's Sons, New York, 1968), shed a great deal of light on the history of the industry. Other books of interest include *Study in Power: John D. Rockefeller, Industrialist and Philanthropist,* Allan Nevins, Charles Scribner's Sons; and

The History of Standard Oil Company, Ida M. Tarbell, McClure, Phillips & Co.

Professor Robert Engler's book, *The Politics of Oil,* The University of Chicago Press, 1961, was also helpful, and I am indebted to the publisher for permission to use some of Engler's material in Chapter 9.

Dr. Howard A. Wilcox of Santa Barbara was gracious enough to permit me to use his research paper exploring alternatives to oil (see Chapter 9), and I am most grateful.

Finally, Dave Dutton of the San Fernando Valley Group, Angeles Chapter, Sierra Club, kindly granted permission to reprint an item in *Conservation Now* (see Chapter 11), a newsletter which Dutton edited.

Part
One

1

The mountains drop sharply to the sea, forming a velvet back-drop for the city. A few miles offshore, islands melt into a hazy blue. Nearly every day cool sea breezes cleanse the air and sweep the valleys as the sea laps gently at sandy beaches, an endless beckoning to the restless soul of man.

Santa Barbara is one of nature's better works of art, an idyllic setting where man can be at peace with the world.

In the midst of that softness, man has imposed a harsh commentary. Huge platforms as high as twenty-story build-ings rise out of the water, towering over the Santa Barbara Channel like awkward toys created by an imaginative youth with a king-size Erector Set. They intrude upon beauty, and they stand as monuments to the frustration of thousands who have tried to make this a cleaner world.

The platforms, which support large derricks, stand on long steel legs in the federal tidelands of the channel. Two of them are operated by Union Oil Company about five miles offshore in water more than 180 feet deep. They are located on one of seventy-one leases that the federal government sold to the oil industry in 1968 for nearly 603 million dollars. Union named its rigs "Platform A" and "Platform B" because they provide work platforms for the drilling crews, and the company planned to erect a third rig on the same lease. In time, plat-forms like "A" and "B" would cover the channel, enabling the oil industry to exploit one of the richest petroleum fields on the North American continent.

In an effort to keep the number of expensive platforms to a

minimum, the industry and the federal government agreed that each rig in the channel would have to be large enough to support at least sixty wells. As a result of that decision, the offshore derricks are much larger than those on land, and, while there may not be as many as there would have been if they had been smaller, their size has made them far more obtrusive.

Now, when the residents of nearby Santa Barbara look seaward toward what was once a beautiful view of the Channel Islands, their eyes focus instead on the manmade monstrosities.

Platforms A and B are located on federal lease No. 402, which covers fifty-four hundred acres. Four oil companies—Union, Gulf, Mobil, and Texaco—paid a whopping $61,-418,000 for the lease, making Tract 402 the most expensive lease in the entire record-breaking auction. Under terms of the contract, Union operates the wells, and the profits are shared among the four companies.

A total of fifty-six wells were to be drilled from Platform A. Workmen had completed drilling the fifth well—called A-21 —on a cool Tuesday morning, January 28, 1969. The well had been completed to a depth of 3479 feet, and the driller had ordered his men to remove the long drill string from the well shaft, called "making a trip." It was a normal operation, done often in the course of drilling a well.

Since oil at the bottom of a new well normally is under intense pressure, it is necessary to block the well to keep the oil from rushing to the surface as the drill is removed from the shaft. This is done by pumping heavy drilling mud down through the hollow drill as the drill is withdrawn. The mud, a combination of thickening chemicals and ordinary mud, flows out openings in the bit at the bottom of the shaft. It fills the shaft as the drill is removed, thus keeping the oil in the reservoir.

The driller finds himself in all kinds of trouble if he fails to pump enough mud down the hole to balance the pressure from the oil. Or if the mud follows the bit up the hole, called "swabbing the hole." Or if the engineer underestimates the pressure at the bottom of the hole.

As the drill string was hauled out of the hole on that January morning, ninety-foot sections were disconnected and swung aside. The bit had been raised about seven hundred feet from the bottom of the hole, and seven sections had been removed at the platform level. The "kelly," which turns the drill string and through which the mud must flow, had been disconnected and swung to the side to permit removal of the eighth section. There had been no problem earlier, and workmen set about their chores in a routine effort to remove another section.

With a frightening roar, mud shot out the top of the eighth stand, ninety feet above the top of the platform. It roared more than twenty feet into the air before it rained down upon the workers. In seconds the platform was so slippery it was almost impossible to stand up, but roustabouts scrambled over the equipment as they desperately sought to stem the flow.

The eighth stand was finally disconnected and set in the pipe racks to clear the way for roustabouts to work on the main opening of the shaft on the rig floor. The mud continued to shoot out of the shaft. Three rig hands grabbed a "threaded preventer" and tried to screw it onto the top of the pipe. They figured that if they could get the preventer on the shaft they could reconnect the kelly and begin pumping more mud down the hole. But they never got a chance. While they were trying to attach the preventer, the last of the mud blasted out of the hole.

A heavy gaseous mist thundered out of the pipe with a roar so loud workmen could not hear each other's frantic yells. The mist engulfed the entire platform, turning it into a terrifying, sickening cloud of potential death while rig hands stumbled about, blinded by the fumes. The attempt to screw in the preventer was abandoned.

A single spark could have turned the platform into a giant torch. Aware of that danger, the crew tried to jam the kelly onto the pipe, but in the turmoil the kelly was damaged, and that effort, too, was abandoned. That left only one possibility. The drill was dropped into the hole and heavy "blind rams" were slammed shut, closing the entire hole.

Drill hands began pumping mud down the shaft through an emergency two-inch line in hopes of building up enough pressure deep in the hole to balance the pressure from the oil. It appeared to workers on the platform that their remaining problems were merely technical; they would have to get enough mud down the hole to permit reopening the shaft on the rig floor. They could then send a "fish" down the shaft and retrieve the drill and complete the well. But it didn't work out that way.

About ten to fifteen minutes after closing the shaft, the drilling engineer noticed bubbles in the ocean around the platform. Moments later huge boils of crude oil began bubbling to the surface about eight hundred feet from the platform. While the men watched, the black mass boiled toward the platform, turning the sea into a two-foot froth. The workers cursed among themselves as gases once again blanketed the area. The tremendous pressure in A-21 had somehow ruptured the bottom of the channel, and all hell was breaking loose. Within a few minutes the gases around the platform became so intense that the men—fearful that an explosion was imminent—were forced to abandon the platform in boats. They did that often in the weeks that followed.

The rupture posed a serious problem for the engineers. They had no way of knowing how the oil was getting from the reservoir to the opening on the channel floor, and thus no way of blocking its passage. And because they had been forced to drop the drill into the shaft, they were unable to pump mud to the bottom of the well. The most they could do at that stage was pump mud into the upper part of the shaft and hope they could force it down to the bottom, somehow blocking the channel through which the oil was reaching the rupture.

As Union's president, Fred Hartley, later told a congressional hearing—in what must be the grandest understatement of the entire fiasco—"We knew immediately, of course, that we had a problem."

Union first reported the "problem" to the Los Angeles office of the U. S. Geological Survey at 1 P.M. on January 28, slightly more than two hours after the well was lost. Regional Supervisor D. W. Solanas was in Casper, Wyoming, on business. He was notified the next day and arrived in Santa Barbara on the morning of January 30.

Experts from the famed Red Adair Fire Fighting Company of Houston arrived in Santa Barbara Thursday morning. The firm is known for its work in fighting oil well fires and blowouts, but the blowout at Platform A proved a good match for Adair's crews, who had been battling a blowout off the coast of Australia during the entire month of December. Adair told reporters that his six-man team of specialists had plugged eleven offshore blowouts during the previous year, from the Persian Gulf to Venezuela.

According to the U. S. Geological Survey, within twenty-four hours after the blowout "oil and gas were seeping vigorously from numerous ocean floor sources along an east–west zone extending from a point about 250 feet west of the platform to a point about 1050 feet east of the platform." That area continued to grow until the zone of seepage measured as much as five hundred feet wide by three-quarters of a mile long. It stretched from a point thirteen hundred feet west of the platform to twenty-six hundred feet east of the platform. Indeed, the floor of the Santa Barbara Channel had ruptured in scores of areas as the oil, under intense pressure, found numerous avenues of escape once the initial damage had been done.

News of the blowout hit Southern California like a thunderclap. Santa Barbara County Supervisor George Clyde, who had been battling the oil interests since they first began eyeing the channel, immediately sent a wire to Secretary of the Interior Walter Hickel. The Secretary was the most controversial member of the new President's cabinet—controversy that would change but not subside—and prior to his confirmation there had been considerable speculation that he would be rejected by the Senate. Hickel, former governor of Alaska, had come under sharp criticism because of his fraternization with friends in the oil industry in his home state, and because he failed to demonstrate as much concern for conservation as his opponents wanted to see in the incoming Secretary of the Interior. The blowout came just four days after he was installed in office.

In his wire to Hickel, Clyde demanded that "all oil drilling in federal waters in Santa Barbara Channel be immediately stopped."

"The current ongoing spill must be stopped," the wire stated. "A complete and thorough investigation to determine if it is possible to continue drilling without additional spills must be made and valid assurances given prior to any resumption of drilling. This request covers not only the platform involved but all other drilling operations in the federal waters."

Hickel replied that he would "continue to keep abreast of developments," and he brushed off Clyde's demand for a drilling halt, apparently believing the matter was not as serious as Clyde had indicated. His wire also reflected an underestimation of the ire of the people of Santa Barbara, the first of a long series of mistakes he was to make in the weeks ahead.

While the ruptures continued to flood the channel with churning boils of black oil, most casual observers thought that somehow the oil industry would be able to remove the oil—or at least dissolve it—before the gunk reached the beaches. But as days passed they began to realize the dismal lack of preparation by the industry. Although there had been repeated warnings during the drilling, and the industry knew there was a substantial chance of leakage, the unbelievable fact forced itself upon the public: The industry was almost totally incapable of doing anything about the oil once it had been released into the channel. Later reports indicated that nearly all of the oil that leaked from the well remained in the water or washed up on one of the beaches or on one of the offshore islands. Only a tiny fraction of the oil was removed from the water, primarily because the oil industry had not developed the equipment to handle such a problem and the government had not bothered to require the industry to do so.

While the growing slick moved like a cloud of doom toward the coastline, workmen at the platform continued their efforts to seal the well. The *Modeco II,* a drilling vessel, was taken to the scene and commenced drilling. Engineers planned to intersect the thirty-five-hundred-foot shaft, hoping to block the passages through which the oil was escaping. And the industry casually informed an enraged public that such an operation could take about three weeks.

The massive slick continued to grow. It had already begun to claim its toll—hundreds of dead birds lying along the beach, their feathers glued together. Hundreds of other birds were saved by emergency treatment centers set up along the beach, but before it was over the death toll among waterfowl ran into the thousands. Union began spraying a detergent on the slick, hoping to dissolve the oil, but conservationists charged that the detergent was even more dangerous to wildlife than the oil. Union executives countered that "they knew what they were doing," but spectators had reason to doubt such a claim.

Secretary Hickel arrived in Santa Barbara for the first time on Sunday, five days after the blowout. By then the slick measured ten by twenty miles, and it blanketed a wide area of the channel. Hickel made an aerial survey aboard a Coast Guard aircraft, conferred with local officials, talked with oil industry executives in one of the city's plush hotels, and pronounced the problem "worse than I anticipated."

In his presence, the county Board of Supervisors passed a resolution calling for an end to all offshore drilling until leaks could be prevented. Hickel sympathized with them, and then suggested that "if there's anything harder to control than oil pollution in water, I don't know what it is." He did not agree to their request.

However, he later asked the oil companies to halt drilling voluntarily until "we can re-evaluate and reassess the situation."

During his brief visit to Santa Barbara, Hickel defended the oil industry and chose instead to place the blame on federal regulations. To many, it was a conclusion that justified much of the criticism leveled at Hickel during the stormy controversy over his appointment.

As Hickel was preparing to leave Santa Barbara, a reporter asked him if he thought the blowout had been caused by negligence.

"No, not at all," said Hickel, disagreeing with many experts in the oil industry. "It is as much the fault of the federal government. The oil company was following federal regulations."

"Is offshore drilling necessary?" he was asked.

"It's not for me to decide. We must always go forward . . . to take care of the thirst of the population."

Hickel, whose formal education ended at high school, had gone to Alaska in 1940 to earn his fortune, and he did just that. He became a multimillionaire building houses, supermarkets, and hotels. A former prize fighter, he fought his way to the governorship of a state that honors strength and guts and that has no time for false fronts. And while he approached the Santa Barbara problem with timidity, that was not to be his style in the years ahead. In time, he would emerge as the rebel in Nixon's generally staid cabinet—a scrappy, cocky fighter whose mouth often got ahead of his brain and who quickly earned notoriety for such statements as "I think we have had a policy of conservation just for conservation purposes."

Two days after Hickel's visit to Santa Barbara, what many had feared came to pass. A tide of crude oil swept past an ineffective boom and into Santa Barbara harbor as shifting winds pushed the scum onto the coast.

It was inevitable. The leak was only one week old, but the massive slick stretched twenty miles down the coast and forty miles to sea, contaminating an eight-hundred-square-mile area that had once been the pride of Southern California yachtsmen. A herd of a hundred seals was trapped on the three small, rocky outcroppings that make up Anacapa Island as the slick completely surrounded the island. And on the mainland, the white sands turned black and the stench drove shoreline residents from their homes.

Meanwhile, it was back to business as usual on the other offshore drilling platforms in the federal tidelands of the channel. Hickel allowed them to resume operations after their plans had been reviewed. It was a stunning maneuver to most observers, who had watched the oil industry prove that it was not only unable to stop the leak, but it was also unable to control the slick once the leak had been created.

One of those who was deeply disturbed was Senator Edmund S. Muskie, Democrat of Maine, who was conducting a hearing of his subcommittee on air and water pollution when he first learned that the Interior Department had authorized resumption of drilling. The key witness at Muskie's hearing at the time he learned of Hickel's decision was, ironically, Union's president Hartley. In a tense but polite exchange of views, Muskie told Hartley:

" . . . You resumed drilling on a decision based upon the judgment of what you describe as experts based on the decision that this kind of thing is not likely to happen again in the places where drilling is now going on. If it does happen, notwithstanding your best judgment, then you will not be in a position to deal with it any more effectively than you have dealt with this one.

"What you have done involves calculated risks. You think they are well calculated. That is your judgment. It is a matter of record. That is all I want to know, but you are in no better position to deal with a repetition of this than you were to deal with this particular incident, as I understand your testimony. That is all I want in the record.

"Whether or not you have acted wisely is something for the future to say . . ."

By February 5, the oil had blackened a twelve-mile stretch of Santa Barbara beaches. Sea birds died by the hundreds, mired in half-inch-deep oil. A wildlife expert termed it the worst disaster to hit California's bird life. Damage mounted into the hundreds of thousands of dollars. Residents living on yachts in the harbor were evacuated as the oil blackened the hulls of seven hundred boats valued at more than five million dollars.

And yet the oil industry, which had decided it was competent to move ahead with offshore operations, was incapable of handling the situation. The best solution that the experts had come up with was to throw straw on the oily waters to absorb the petroleum. Huge piles of oil-soaked straw appeared on the beach, monuments to the havoc that man had reaped upon the coastline.

More than one thousand men and 125 pieces of equipment worked on the beaches—at a cost of five thousand dollars per mile—and it took fifty-two-hundred truckloads to carry the oil-soaked straw and other debris to three landfill sites east and west of Santa Barbara. The burning of additional material was halted because the stench and smoke were intolerable.

Out at sea, crewmen continued their efforts to stem the flow of oil from the seafloor ruptures, abandoning their platform when the gases became too dangerous, and then returning when the winds swept the fumes away for a while.

And all along the beach, a drama of death continued to unfold. During the first two months of the spill, at least thirty-six hundred birds died as a result of the pollution, according to a study by the Pacific Northwest Laboratories of Battelle Memorial Institute at Richland, Washington. But there were more subtle results that in the long run may have a profound effect upon the ecology of the channel. In testimony before the U. S. Senate antitrust and monopoly subcommittee, Dr. Max Blumer of the Woods Hole Oceanographic Institution gave some indication of what happens when oil spills into the sea.

"From laboratory studies on oil and oil products, and on many marine animals, we have determined that all crude oils and all oil products—excepting some highly purified substances—are poisons for all marine organisms," Dr. Blumer testified. "In addition to direct killing, the destruction of sensitive juvenile forms and the depletion of food resources, oils act on marine life in more subtle ways. The incorporation of sublethal amounts of oil leads to reduced resistance to stress and may result in failure to reproduce.

"Research prompted by a high incidence of skin cancer in some refinery personnel had traced the cause to prolonged skin contact with petroleum and refinery products.

"We have shown that marine organisms ingest and retain hydrocarbons to which they are exposed. These are transferred to and retained by predators. In this way even animals that were not directly exposed to a spill can become polluted by eating contaminated animals. This and the presence of cancer-causing chemicals in oil production implies that the marketing and eating of fish and shellfish from polluted areas may constitute a public health hazard.

"The most immediately toxic fractions of oil and oil products are soluble in sea water; therefore, biological damage will occur at the very moment of the accident. Water currents will immediately spread the toxic plume of dissolved oil components and, if the accident occurs in inshore water, the whole water column will be poisoned even if the bulk of the oil floats on the surface."

Dr. Blumer testified that research had confirmed that "Where oil can be detected in the sediments there has been a kill of animal life; in the most polluted areas the kill has been almost total, while in control stations outside the area there are normal, healthy bottom fauna."

The research which led to Dr. Blumer's conclusions mainly involved refined oils, such as diesel fuel. Since the Santa Barbara oil spill of 1969, scores of research projects have

been conducted by numerous universities and private founda-
tions, and it has been established that oil varies in its toxicity.
Diesel fuel, for example, is far more poisonous to marine
life than is crude oil. Massive spills of diesel fuel on the East
Coast and off the coast of Baja California have had a catastrophic impact on the ecology, due primarily to the toxicity
of the fuel.

Crude oil, on the other hand, has been found to be less
toxic than the more refined oil products. The most dramatic
effect of crude oil—as well as other heavy oils—has been
mechanical rather than chemical. In other words, most marine organisms killed in spills of crude oil die because they
are smothered, as in the case of bottom life buried under
the oil, or strangled, as in the case of birds which ingest
the oil while trying to clean their feathers, thus clogging
their respiratory systems.

The death scene along the banks of the channel during the
spill added fuel to the fires that were burning elsewhere in
Santa Barbara.

"People are mad," Mayor Gerald Firestone told reporters
as he stood next to the black waters of the channel. "You bet
they're mad. This city is known throughout the world as a
beautiful community. Look at it now. We have laws which
prohibit oil drilling within the city limits. But what can we do
about this? This comes from outside."

Meanwhile, workmen, hampered by torrential rains and
brisk winds, continued their efforts to plug the leaks beneath Platform A. Drilling mud was imported from throughout the state. Barges arrived at the platform around the clock,
and mud was pumped into the well at rates of up to thirty
barrels per mintue, forced down the shaft with pressures ranging up to thirty-seven-hundred pounds per square inch. After
seven thousand barrels of mud had been injected into the
well, workers noticed a marked decrease in the amount of oil
boiling to the surface. That was February 7, eleven days after
the blowout. Plans were made to cement the well closed per-

manently, and Union's president Hartley announced that the battle had been won.

There would be limited seepage for a while, Hartley said, but the main flow had been stopped. But, as the days rolled on, more leaks appeared and oil continued to wash ashore as the industry demonstrated that it still was unable to handle the problem.

The words of Senator Muskie must have haunted the oil executive from time to time, although his public pronouncements failed to show any great degree of concern. By the end of March, less than two months after the blowout, most of the mainland shores of the Santa Barbara Channel and some areas of the Channel Islands had been affected by the oil, according to a report by the Allan Hancock Foundation of the University of Southern California. By the end of July, no mainland beach in the channel had escaped the spill.

The days came and went, and oil continued to gurgle to the surface, first from one source and then from another, and the industry continued to demonstrate its impotence. But in the chambers of city offices, and in the boardroom of the county supervisors, and in the homes of residents and conservationists throughout Southern California, the move was anything but impotent.

As Gladwin Hill of the New York *Times* put it, the oil industry had fired the "ecological shot heard round the world." Thousands had decided to make their stand. The issues in Santa Barbara were basic. Was this nation ready to sacrifice one of its most precious natural resources—the coastline of California—for sheer monetary gain?

Man had once again left his soiled footprints across one of nature's most valuable gifts. For smog-weary Southern California, and for a nation awakening to the fact that man may indeed be destroying the delicate ecological balance of the world in which he lives, the blowout at Platform A was just too much.

Soon after the blowout, more than one-hundred-thousand

signatures were collected on petitions calling for an end to offshore drilling. The cause of conservation was carried across the nation and into the citadels of power by political leaders who picked up the increasingly popular banner of ecology.

Stewart Udall, who was Secretary of the Interior when the leases were sold, later grieved over the mistake. His decision to approve drilling in the channel was a "conservation Bay of Pigs," he said during a speech before an ecology conference in Oakland eight months after the blowout.

President Richard Nixon, himself a native of California, months later expressed it as well as anyone, though perhaps inadvertently:

"Will future generations say of us that we were the richest nation and the ugliest land in all history?" the President asked.

Millions of Americans, disturbed by what they had seen at Santa Barbara, decided it did not have to be that way. Largely because of the blowout at Platform A, this nation could never again talk about conservation in the complacent tones it once had used.

But in many ways it was to be a losing battle.

The blowout at Platform A was a blatant form of pollution because it was the product of one thing: Greed. It would seem, then, that if the people of California—and the rest of the nation, for that matter—decided it was not worth sacrificing the precious and dwindling seashore for the profits of one industry it would be a simple matter to end offshore drilling. Not so.

During the long hearings that followed the blowout, the soul of the petroleum industry was laid bare. Hartley went to great lengths during a congressional hearing to explain that the oil industry and the federal government are partners, since each needs the other. No one, perhaps not even Hartley, knew at that time just how firm that partnership really was.

The oil industry has emerged as the most powerful industry in this nation. It has resisted control on every level. It has established interlocking interests with state, local, and federal governmental agencies. It has installed its own people in high places. It is the world's leading polluter.

And it, perhaps more than any other industry, had demonstrated why we are losing our battle to stop poisoning the world in which we live.

2

California is a haven for the unusual. It is home to many whose lifestyles are strange. It tolerates that which is different, from the speed freaks of San Francisco's drug culture to the gaudy artificialities of filmdom where the weird and the perverse are the standards, not the exceptions.

It is the home of Disneyland, a plastic reminder of the past where Mickey Mouse still reigns supreme, and where the social injustices that plague most of America fade into oblivion. What other state could accommodate both Disneyland and Forest Lawn Memorial Park, a cemetery where more than fifty thousand couples have exchanged their wedding vows? What other state has elected a former movie actor as governor and sent an old soft shoe shuffler to the United States Senate?

To millions who do not live there, California is a Shangri-La, where affluence is within easy reach of every man. Thousands migrate there every year, most in search of a better life, and others because they see in California something they cannot find anywhere else.

But California is more than all of this. The elusive vistas have been blacktopped to serve the modern king of paradise lost—the automobile. Unemployment lines are legendary; the cost of living is astronomical; urban blight is appalling; and the natural attractions that millions sought when they moved to California are disappearing in the holy name of progress.

There was a time, long ago, when people who could afford to live anywhere chose to live on Orange Grove Avenue in Pasadena, just east of Los Angeles. The San Gabriel Mountains towered over the stately mansions along Millionaire's Row, and the magnificent homes seemed sheltered from the world as they stood in the shade of splendid trees. But as the years passed, the nearby mountains disappeared behind a curtain of smog, the millionaires moved on, and the spectacular old homes were converted into apartments.

Much of the state's coastline was transformed into an industrial wasteland. Many beaches were fenced off as "private." By 1970, less than ninety miles of the state's entire coastline belonged to the people—and much of that was contaminated.

Workers who had moved to California in search of a better life soon found that employment often entailed driving for an hour or more to and from work. Air pollution, that nauseating commentary on man and his willful destruction of his environment, spread from Los Angeles to other parts of the state. In most areas, there was no escape from the eye-stinging, blinding smog.

Events of recent years forced California to take a long, hard look at itself: The population had grown too much, too fast. The disadvantages of being a Californian were beginning to outweigh the advantages.

There is, of course, a brighter side of the picture.

California still has an unusually good climate, even if the air does look a little peculiar much of the time. Most workers in the state are paid better than in most other states, and the standard of living is relatively high. The rate of growth has dropped a little, to the profound disappointment of developers and land speculators who have raped the countryside.

On weekends, California's amazing freeway system takes on a whole new dimension. Many of the climate-controlled sedans are replaced with "recreation vehicles" as families, head for the great outdoors. This is especially true in Southern California, where suffocating cities force residents to seek a slower pace in hopes of recapturing their own identity. U. S. 101, which heads north out of Los Angeles, is almost as crowded on Saturday morning as it is during the weekday rush hours. The highway, which includes part of the Hollywood and Ventura Freeways, cuts through miles and miles of hillsides covered with homes. The freeway eventually winds through the Conejo Valley and down to the coast. The highway slices along the shore, past small beach cottages, and through a contrasting stretch which the oil industry has uglified with row after row of pumps, storage tanks, derricks, and blackened hillsides.

Bikini-clad surfers, male and female, stand among the oil pumps with their surfboards at the ready, waiting for the right waves. A few hundred feet offshore, a manmade island sticks out of the water. It was built by the oil industry as a permanent platform for offshore operations. The companies stuck a few palm trees on the rocky island, mustered up their collective imagination, and named it "Palm Island."

A few miles farther north, the coastline resumes it natural beauty. Finally, about an hour and a half north of downtown Los Angeles, the hills on the right of the highway rise sharply toward the sky. The rocky coastline puts on a spectacular face. Gorgeous evergreens tower over the highway.

Since the first mission was founded on a hill overlooking the sea in 1782, Santa Barbara has seemed like another world. Over the years the city matured gracefully while much of the nation struggled with growing pains. The rich and the proud and the beautiful moved there, covering the hillsides with stately mansions, and preserving the natural beauty of the long, white beaches. The city's scenery was enhanced by fine buildings that reflected the Spanish heritage of the community. Red tile roofs contrasted sharply with the green hillsides and the blue skies, and Santa Barbara took on an identity all its own.

Many years ago, at least half of the people who lived there were independently wealthy. They had made their fortunes elsewhere and moved to Santa Barbara to enjoy the fruits of their labors. The rest lived there because they could not stand the thought of living anywhere else. They worked on the fishing boats that plied the waters of the channel, or they opened small shops near the waterfront to capture a share of the tourist trade, or they earned a living as public servants or schoolteachers. In time, that changed too. The super-rich dwindled to about a dozen families, and many who had opened small stores prospered through the growing flow of visitors from throughout California. The gap narrowed.

Several years ago, a new element moved into Santa Barbara —the "think tank." Such organizations as the now-famous Center for the Study of Democratic Institutions brought personalities like the late rebel bishop James Pike to Santa Barbara to work toward solving the profound problems of a troubled nation. Santa Barbara's campus of the University of California brought other scholars into the community. The city gladly opened its doors to such institutions, but emphatically said "no" to anyone who threatened to bring noise, pollution, or ugliness to the area.

Santa Barbara had been threatened repeatedly over the years, by nature as well as by man. An earthquake destroyed much of the community in 1925, but the city fathers treated the earthquake as though it had been a God-sent urban renewal project, and Santa Barbara rose out of the rubble as a better city. In more recent years, the city has been threatened at least twice by major brush fires, which roared over the mountains and down to the city. A few homes were lost, but the people managed to avert total disaster.

Everyone saw the danger of fire and earthquake, but in the beginning only the most astute foresaw that the city was approaching another threat of far more devastating potential. Oil had been discovered in Southern California.

Wildcatters moved across the state like locusts, eager to probe the earth's bowels wherever they could set up their equipment. There were various ways of determining where oil was likely to be found but, then as well as now, there was only one way to find out if the oil was actually there—by drilling. Huge oil deposits were discovered in sun-parched Kern County about a hundred miles east of Santa Barbara, and the barren hills around Bakersfield sprouted derricks as though they were desert Joshua trees. The Long Beach area, just south of Los Angeles, also turned out to be rich with oil, and derricks sprang up in backyards and along the waterfront. Rich deposits were found in the Ventura area, about midway between Los Angeles and Santa Barbara.

The wildcatters had every reason to believe that the oil-bearing strata continued up the coast and into Santa Barbara, and they expected an eager welcome from the city when they arrived there in 1946 to begin their explorations. The oilmen felt that the greatest deposits were offshore, and they petitioned the city for permission to drill in the Santa Barbara Channel. To their astonishment, the city said "no."

As the years passed, the state's oil industry grew stronger, and it became apparent that the entire Santa Barbara area was probably rich with oil. That knowledge put the city in a strange dilemma. Should the community relax its "no oil" stance just enough to get in on the boom, or should it continue to say "no" to a source of new wealth? In early 1960, city councilmen who were feeling the pinch of conservative pocketbooks decided to take a closer look. The council voted to launch a study into the possibility of leasing four onshore parcels for oil exploration.

But before the study could get off the ground, Santa Barbara erupted with the kind of fury that had not been seen since the 1925 earthquake. But this time it came from the residents, not nature. There were threats to recall the entire council if the study went through, and the councilmen could see that the threats were backed by most of their constituents. The study never began.

The people of Santa Barbara thought they had won. Their government had been responsive to their demands. But what they did not know was that a new era was dawning.

Actually, the new era had started more than two decades earlier, when the nation first came to grips with the problem of tideland ownership. That is one of those problems that drive laymen crazy and send political writers into fits of ecstasy. It is fraught with inconsistency, confusion, controversy, and irony. The issue dates back to the 1940s, when Gulf Coast states, particularly Louisiana and Texas, decided that the tidelands belonged to the individual states, not the federal government. Both states entered into agreements with the oil industry for offshore oil exploration, but the United States Supreme Court ruled against them. The high court decided that states could not claim jurisdiction beyond the three-mile limit, and that the continental shelf, beyond three miles, belonged to the nation, not the states.

That decision brought a cry of outrage from the oil industry and from the states of Louisiana, Texas, and California, all of whom stood to lose millions in oil revenues. A bill was passed by the U. S. Congress, returning the shelf to the contiguous states, but it was vetoed in 1946 by President Harry Truman. But a short time later a new man entered the picture.

Russell Billiu Long was the son of Senator Huey Pierce Long, the Louisiana "Kingfish" whose unruly behavior dominated the floor of the United States Senate until he was assassinated in 1935 by Dr. Carl A. Weiss, who was immediately slain by the senator's bodyguards. After a stint in the Navy, the younger Long joined the staff of his rambunctious uncle, Earl Long, then governor of Louisiana. But in 1948, Senator Jon Overton died, and Russell wanted the job. Since he had not yet reached the minimum age of thirty, Governor Long made an interim appointment and held the post open until Russell was old enough to make the race.

As an assistant to his uncle, the governor, Russell had helped establish a big, new levy on gas and oil extraction in Louisiana, thus earning the opposition of the state's powerful oil interests when he ran for the Senate. He won on the basis of a backwoods vote that had supported his father and his uncle, and because he had one of the most famous surnames in the history of the South. But he won by a narrow margin of ten thousand out of a half-million votes. It was the last time he opposed the oil industry, and the last time he had any trouble winning an election in Louisiana.

He joined the Senate in 1948 as its youngest member and one of two freshman senators. The other was Hubert Horatio Humphrey of Minnesota, age thirty-seven. They made their first appearance on the Senate floor on the same day, during a filibuster against President Truman's civil rights legislation. Humphrey had obtained special permission to break into the filibuster, and he spoke in favor of a federal power project badly needed in the Missouri Valley. Long followed, and he reopened the filibuster, launching his career with an attempt to preserve the status quo.

Over the years Long became one of the most influential men in the Senate, rising to the chairmanship of the powerful Senate Finance Committee. He also aligned himself more closely with the oil industry, and grew richer with income from oil and gas production on his Louisiana property. It never seemed to bother the senator that he personally profited from his official actions—such as receiving nearly half a million dollars in tax-free income over a six-year period because of the outrageous oil depletion allowance, which he fought to preserve (see Chapter 10).

In 1969, when the depletion allowance came under especially strong attack, Long looked at his position and concluded, as quoted by the Associated Press:

"A long time ago I became convinced that if you have financial interests completely parallel to your state, then you have no problem. My state produces more oil and gas per acre than any other state in the Union. If I didn't represent the oil and gas industry, I wouldn't represent the state of Louisiana."

Thus with a shrug of his shoulders and through simple economics he dismissed the fact that the will of the industry might indeed clash with the good of his state.

Be that as it may, Long's star in the United States Senate continued to rise, not only because he had the backing of the world's most powerful industry, but because of the nature of Russell Billiu Long himself. Long portrays himself as the friend of "the little guy," and his record in the Senate partly backs that contention. He supported most welfare bills and he sponsored numerous bills to increase Social Security payments, although he consistently opposed civil rights legislation.

The battle over who owns the continental shelf had already begun when Long entered the Senate, and he made it one of his special projects. For more than a decade he stormed through the Senate, charging that any attempt by the federal government to stop the states from exploiting the shelf would be a violation of "states' rights."

What the senator did not say, of course, was that the oil industry wanted the power vested in the states rather than the federal government because it would have been cheaper and easier to control the individual states than the federal government. Long sponsored several bills, all backed by the oil industry, but in the end he lost. Or so he thought.

In 1953 the U. S. Congress passed legislation giving the federal government the right to administer oil and gas leases on the submerged lands seaward of the three-mile limit. Long bitterly denounced the legislation, claiming it would give the federal government a "virtual dictatorship."

The law "does great violence to our traditional concept of dual sovereignty," Long charged, "and will, insofar as law and order are concerned, create a virtual dictatorship which will impose its heavy hand at will on the administration of justice to many thousands of American citizens."

What he did not know at that time, of course, was that the "dictatorship" would work to the profound advantage of the oil industry. The industry had been right on one point—the federal government commanded a bigger slice of the profits than some of the states; and wrong on another—the federal government was not harder to control, as evidenced years later in Santa Barbara.

By giving the power to the federal government, the 1953 legislation greatly diminished control of offshore operations by local governments. Seaboard communities like Santa Barbara were virtually powerless to control the industry beyond the three-mile limit. There is sound evidence that it would have been different if the state of California had retained control.

In 1955, the California state legislature enacted the Shell-Cunningham Act, which set up an offshore sanctuary for sixteen miles along the Santa Barbara coastline. The sanctuary banned all drilling within the area, which extended out to the three-mile limit, which was as far as the state's authority extended under the new federal statute.

The sanctuary was established because the people of Santa Barbara convinced their duly elected state representatives that the city wanted its coastline left unspoiled. This is all particularly significant in view of the fact that the city would have received a percentage of the royalties from any oil or gas production within the sanctuary, as per state laws governing the state tidelands. They had decided to forgo the money and keep their coastline instead.

When it became apparent that the federal government planned to lease tracts in the federal tidelands, the people of Santa Barbara rose up in arms and fought to have their sanctuary extended to the Channel Islands, about twenty miles offshore. But the federal government refused. Santa Barbara, which would receive no royalties from federal leases, would lose its coastline anyway through a strange twist of irony. Legislation that the oil industry had so vigorously opposed had worked to the benefit of the industry and to the detriment of the people.

The federal government did, however, agree to honor a limited extension of the state sanctuary. Under the law, the federal government could grant leases from three miles out, but in the Santa Barbara case the Department of Interior made one concession. No leases were granted within two miles of the sanctuary.

It was a trivial victory for the people of Santa Barbara. The city had wanted its natural beauty protected; but the federal government and the industry wanted the oil beneath the quiet waters of the Santa Barbara Channel. There was sound evidence in California that both goals could not be satisfied. Proof of that could be found about one hundred miles south of Santa Barbara, in the city of Long Beach.

There was a time, long, long ago, when Long Beach was everything its name implied: a long beach with clean sand and rolling surf. But years ago the people of Long Beach and the state of California sold that birthright to the oil industry. The city, which shared in the royalties, grew richer as the black gold was extracted from beneath its soil, but it also grew uglier. Oil derricks sprang up along the coastline, turning that once-beautiful seascape into an incongruous jungle of steel and concrete. The derricks were joined by oil refineries, which helped turn the air black with smog. Over the years the city literally sank lower and lower as the oil was extracted—in some places dropping nearly thirty feet—leaving other scars.

More recently, the story of Long Beach took its most telling turn. The oil-rich city purchased the aging oceanliner *Queen Mary* with the intention of restoring elegance to the old lady of the seas and turning the ship into a mecca for tourists. After several years of controversy, lawsuits, and mismanagement, the city has spent nearly fifty million dollars on the old bucket. And while the new dressings may reflect some of the regal splendor of the queen's past, the ship symbolizes the terrible price the people of Long Beach have paid for civic affluence.

The ship is moored in the city's harbor along the blackened flatlands where the oil derricks reign supreme. The queen's throne is in an outhouse.

With that kind of heritage, a reasonable man might wonder why the oil industry would even consider attacking an area like Santa Barbara. The answers are both complex and simple:

The primary reason—the simple one—is that oil production is extremely profitable, and the oil industry is in business to make money. In this country, for reasons that will be discussed more fully later, it is not easy to lose money on oil production, regardless of the cost. Corporate profits within the industry have been quite high in recent years, ranging around an 11 or 12 percent return on the investment. Most corporations in other fields are content with less.

But there are more complex reasons, and they involve not only the industry but the federal government as well—and every single person who lives in this country. This nation's appetite for petroleum, and the long list of petroleum products, is astonishing. The United States produces more oil than any other single nation in the world, yet it uses considerably more than it produces. In 1970, the country had to import about 20 percent of its oil. Without petroleum, life as we know it would grind toward a halt. It is the primary source of energy, and it will continue to be the main source for many years to come.

The ideal situation for any country is to be self-sufficient when it comes to energy, and of all the world's industrial nations the United States probably comes closest to reaching that ideal. Nations that are forced to rely heavily upon imported oil—and this is true for nearly all of Western Europe —are subjected to the whims and fancies of foreign governments and international conflicts. The Middle East, that hotbed of international intrigue where most of the world's proved oil reserves are found, supplies most of the oil for Western Europe. It is little wonder that those otherwise relatively uninfluential little Mideast countries, through their ability to curb the flow of oil, account for ulcers around the world.

Seven companies dominate the worldwide oil industry. Five of the seven are U.S. companies: Standard of New Jersey, Mobil, Texaco, Gulf, and Standard of California. The other two are British Petroleum and Shell.

Since the industries control the worldwide retail outlets, they can cope with the political whims of unstable governments better than they like to admit. Oil in the ground is of little value to anyone, and producing countries rely upon the industry to extract the oil and sell it on the international market. Thus foreign governments may make life unpleasant for the industry from time to time, but terms are usually reached, as in the Middle East crisis of 1971.

When Dwight D. Eisenhower was President of the United States, it troubled him deeply to see the nation dependent upon foreign oil. As a military man, he knew that one of the reasons Germany lost World War II was that it ran so low on oil it was unable to operate many of its implements of destruction. The retired general decided it would be to the nation's interest to cut down on its dependence upon foreign oil, and on March 10, 1959, he established the oil import quota system.

In general terms, the import program restricted imports for the area east of the Rocky Mountains to 12.2 percent of the total domestic production. It restricted imports on the West Coast to whatever was necessary to make up the difference beween production and consumption. In recent years, imports for both the east and west have totaled more than 20 percent.

The program has had a profound impact upon the industry and the nation. It was fought at first by the major oil companies that had invested heavily in foreign oil with the intention of selling their cheaper imports at considerable profit in the United States. But, like the tidelands controversy, over the years the import program has worked to the benefit of the industry. It set up a protective market within the United States, making it profitable for the oil industry to conduct costly operations and then sell its products to a captive audience.

Eisenhower had hoped that the quota system would entice the industry to find new reserves in the continental limits of the United States. But new drilling and wildcat operations continued a downward trend, which had begun in 1956, dropping from a high that year of 58,160 new wells to a low of 8878 wells in 1967. The reason for the drop has been blamed on many things, but most experts believe drilling declined because most of the land mass had been thoroughly explored.

That left only one place to go. The American Petroleum Institute estimated in late 1969 that only about 1 percent of the seabed surrounding the continent had been tested for petroleum. The institute, in a paper entitled "Offshore Petroleum and the Environment," estimated that "the total recoverable reserves underlying the U.S. continental shelf may be over two hundred billion barrels of oil and more than one thousand trillion cubic feet of natural gas—a potential great enough to supply U.S. needs for many years to come."

Experts agreed that extracting the oil from beneath the shelf would be extremely expensive. Offshore drilling platforms alone could run as high as eighteen million dollars, the institute predicted. But what the institute did not say, of course, was that it would be worth it to the industry to make that kind of investment. President Eisenhower's well-meaning intentions had set up the consumer in this nation to pay whatever it required for the oil industry to extract petroleum and make a profit.

In 1970, about 13 percent of the nation's oil and gas came from offshore wells, mostly in the Gulf of Mexico and in the waters of the Pacific off Southern California. Very little exploration had been conducted off the Atlantic coast, but the petroleum institute speculated that the eastern continental shelf "is also thought to have significant petroleum potential."

"Thus far, the U.S. petroleum industry has invested an estimated thirteen billion dollars in the search for and development of offshore deposits of oil and natural gas, and operating costs are adding to this total at a daily rate of two million dollars. Many companies operating offshore have not yet begun to break even—all told, offshore petroleum operations show an earnings deficit of an estimated 7.5 billion dollars," according to the institute.

However, there is the possibility of one tremendous economic advantage in offshore drilling. After any oil well begins producing, it would seem logical that most of the oil could be removed from the reservoir. But that is far from true. In many cases only about 5 percent of the oil is recoverable. That figure is considerably higher in other cases, but the average for all wells in the United States is around 20 percent. Beyond that point it costs more to get the oil out than it is worth.

But there is evidence that the recovery rate may be considerably higher in offshore production. In 1968 the U. S. Department of the Interior published a booklet called *United States Petroleum through 1980*. That publication noted that a recovery rate of 45 to 50 percent is normally expected from wells off the coast of Louisiana. That percentage probably will not hold true for the entire continental shelf, but it is an encouraging factor for the oil industry, and it may help explain why the industry is willing to lay out such a bundle for offshore drilling.

From a purely military standpoint, President Eisenhower's plan to make the United States self-sufficient was not without its faults. During World War II, with massive battles in both the Pacific and Atlantic theaters, this nation still managed to import much of its oil, mostly from Venezuela, where one of the largest oil fields in the world is located. There have been vast new discoveries all over the world since the war ended, and even leaders within the oil industry have admitted that it is absurd to think that all foreign sources might be cut off during a time of international crisis.

Just for the sake of argument, if all foreign sources were closed to this nation, it would still be possible to meet the country's needs by increasing the rate of production and by producing synthetic substitutes for petroleum. That would be possible unless, of course, this nation had already exhausted its oil reserves. Thus Eisenhower's logic, if carried through, would dictate that in terms of national security conservation of resources is perhaps far more important than the exploitation of resources. What kind of situation will this country find itself in if at some time it is forced to depend solely upon domestic sources that were exhausted during a time of peace?

Thus under the guise of national security, the federal government paved the way for the domestic oil industry to exploit the continental shelf. And there were still other reasons why the oil industry found that prospect so attractive.

As of 1970, nearly half of the people in this country lived in counties bordering the coastlines. This trend is expected to continue as more and more citizens migrate to population centers along the Pacific, Atlantic, and Gulf coasts. If the oil industry exploited the resources beneath the continental shelf, it would have the added advantage of producing and refining the petroleum close to the markets. The cost of transporting the oil would drop dramatically, thus helping to balance the cost of offshore operations.

Unfortunately, it took the blowout at Platform A to force public officials to realize that the prospects were not as rosy as they seemed. The second report of the President's Panel on Oil Spills, issued in 1969 as a direct result of the Santa Barbara blowout, offered these disturbing observations:

"Since 1954, approximately eight thousand offshore wells have been drilled. Twenty-five blowouts have occurred, of which seventeen leaked gas only. Two resulted in serious oil pollution incidents and nine constituted serious blowouts that persisted for several days with fires (nine cases) or fire hazards and hazards to personnel (twenty-nine deaths). If offshore development continues to expand at the present rate and the frequency of accidents remains the same, three thousand to five thousand wells will be drilled annually by 1980 and we can expect to have a major pollution incident somewhere every year.

"There ought to be a choice whereby it is possible to set aside resources which may be developed eventually but which by conscious choice, and after examination of all interests and values, should not be exploited now," the report continued. "This is conservation in its truest sense. Most estimates of future energy usage indicate that oil and gas consumption will reach its peak within twenty years and that thereafter the energy usage derived from liquid petroleum reserves will decline. Even then our need for oil both for energy and for the ever-growing petrochemical industry will be high. Under these circumstances it does not appear that postponing exploitation of some resources would diminish their value. On the contrary, postponing some of our development might serve best the future of our country."

The report also noted that suboceanic resources represent the largest single area of mineral resources within the boundaries of the United States that we have not yet developed. This fact alone should cause us to exercise special care that we make use of them as wisely as possible. The coastal waters in which they occur are also the site of heavy commercial traffic, recreation, and natural beauty, a unique ecological setting in which exist kinds and types of wildlife that cannot exist elsewhere, and an environment difficult for man to work in. These areas and these resources are the property of all the people. All of their needs and wishes should be considered when deciding on the use of the resources.

It is unfortunate that such wisdom had not prevailed in the fall of 1967, when the people of Santa Barbara were making a desperate attempt to persuade the federal government against offering leases off their coast. On September 22 of that year, city and county officials made a last-ditch effort in a meeting with federal representatives in the chambers of the county Board of Supervisors. Local officials wanted broader public hearings on the matter. The federal government refused. It was a fiery session, climaxed by charges that the federal government was moving too quickly and did not understand what was happening.

At the end of the stormy, two-hour session, Harry Anderson, Assistant Secretary of the Interior for Mineral Resources, squared himself off in front of the local officials and told them that if they had anything else to say they should submit it in writing "in the next few days." As the Santa Barbara officials filed out of the room they knew they had lost. They had failed to show the federal government it was making a tragic mistake, and they knew they had virtually no voice in a decision that would scar their community for decades.

On December 21, 1967, the Department of the Interior announced that leases would be offered during competitive bidding on February 6, 1968. Later, the department admitted that at that time it had no idea just what the leases were worth. Testimony by department officials before the House appropriations subcommittee revealed that oil companies had refused to share their seismic findings with the government, claiming the data comprised "trade secrets." William T. Pecora, Director of the U. S. Geological Survey, admitted that the federal government was "flying partly blind" because it knew only what the oil companies wanted it to know.

The decision to offer the leases was a terrible blow to Santa Barbara, and a boon to the domestic oil industry. One unnamed oil company official was quoted in the Los Angeles *Times* as stating that "the industry got everything it wanted. We came out smelling like a rose."

The government offered a total of 110 lease blocks, each comprising 5760 acres or nine square miles. The leases, granted under the authority of the Outer Continental Shelf Lands Act, were for five years "and so long thereafter as oil or gas may be produced from the leased area in paying quantities, or drilling or well reworking operations, as approved by the Secretary [of the Interior], are conducted thereon." In addition to the "bonuses"—the flat bid paid by the winning companies for each lease—the federal government was to receive 16.67 percent royalty on all oil and gas produced. The companies were also required to pay an annual rental of three dollars per acre.

The federal terms were better than the state of California had required for offshore leases in state waters in the Long Beach and Ventura areas. The state established a sliding scale for the royalties, starting at 16.67 percent and climbing as high as 50 percent, depending upon the rate of production.

Winners of federal leases were required to pay 20 percent of the bonus at the time of the bid, and the remaining 80 percent within thirty days. No operations could be conducted until the entire bonus was paid.

The federal government estimated that the leases would bring in a total of about three hundred million dollars in bonuses, but few people were ready for the drama that unfolded on February 6, in the Renaissance Room of the Biltmore Hotel in downtown Los Angeles. More than five hundred oilmen from across the nation gathered for a tense session where fortune rose and fell with the drop of a gavel.

Oil company executives, who had been waiting for that moment for about two decades, gathered at the hotel even before the sealed bids were submitted at 9 A.M. Plush suites were converted into crash pads for the rich and the powerful who gathered for the spectacle. They wandered around, swapping jokes and trying to ease the tension.

But as the magic moment approached they gathered in the gaudy old Renaissance Room. The roar of small talk grew quieter, and at 10 A.M. a hushed silence fell over the room. William Grant, manager of the Los Angeles office of the Bureau of Land Management, began opening the bids. The first few bids were about what everybody had expected, consisting of tracts fifteen to twenty miles offshore, near the Channel Islands. But as Grant opened more envelopes the bids grew higher and expectations rose.

Humble Oil and Refining Company emerged early as the "hawk." Humble, which had recently opened a new seventy-two-thousand-barrel-per-day refinery north of San Francisco, let it be known early in the game that it counted on a lion's share of the leases. It was estimated that Humble "exposed" by itself or with its partners more than four hundred million dollars in the sale.

One disgruntled oilman turned to a Humble executive and growled, "Why didn't you buy the rest of the state?"

On one lease Humble bid $11,600,640, or $2014 per acre, against an offer by Mobil Oil Corporation and Union of $1,012,000, or $175 per acre. The disparity brought an amazed gasp from the audience. The difference between the high bid and the next bid is called "leaving money on the table," and before the day was over Humble left the table well laden.

One area of special interest was the district just off Rincon Point, several miles south of Santa Barbara, believed to be one of the richest areas in the entire channel. Two tracts there were coveted, No. 401 and No. 402.

A hush fell over the audience as the bids on 401 were opened. A joint venture headed by Superior Oil Company won with a bid of thirty-eight million dollars. That left only Tract 402.

The first bid for 402 was from a group headed by Continental Oil—eighteen million dollars. Humble brought a gasp from the oilmen when it offered fifty-five million dollars. Shell Oil Company's bid of twenty-two million dollars was next, but it was out of the running. Finally, the last bid was opened. It was a joint offer by Union, Gulf, Mobil, and Texaco. The bid was a record sixty-one million dollars.

For a moment, there was a stunned silence. Then wild cheering. No one knew at that ecstatic moment, of course, that less than a year later Tract 402 would rupture beneath Platform A, spewing black muck into the waters of the channel and electrifying conservationists across the nation and around the world.

When the last bid was opened on that Tuesday morning of 1968, the federal government added up the figures. More than two dozen oil companies had paid over 602 million dollars for the rights to drill on seventy-one leases in the channel. That was more than twice the amount expected by the government, and it exceeded the record 510 million dollars the industry had paid for a lease sale the preceding June in the Gulf of Mexico off Louisiana.

Humble, a Houston-based subsidiary of Standard Oil Company of New Jersey, was the big winner, capturing all or part interest in forty-seven tracts at a cost of 217 million dollars. Other big spenders were Union, seventy-six million dollars, with interest in seventeen tracts; Mobil, fifty-five million dollars, fourteen tracts; Gulf, fifty-four million dollars, eleven tracts; Texaco, fifty million dollars, nine tracts; Standard of California, twenty-five million dollars, thirty-one tracts; Atlantic Richfield, eight million dollars, fourteen tracts.

Shell Oil Company, the British-Dutch giant, had been the big winner in the Louisiana sale, but it bid on a number of leases in the Santa Barbara Channel and won only one. It was, some oilmen said, poetic justice, since Shell had left very few leases for other companies during the Louisiana sale.

The huge sale reverberated around the world. Global Marine, Inc., of Los Angeles, one of the world's leading corporations in offshore exploration, immediately recalled one of its drilling vessels from the Panama Canal, where it was on its way to the Gulf Coast.

Several companies paid their bonuses immediately and began moving equipment into the channel within a few hours.

It was a sobering experience for Santa Barbara. The amount of money that the industry had been willing to lay down for the leases proved that the channel contained some of the richest oil deposits in the western United States. The stakes were extremely high.

Federal leases in the Santa Barbara Channel should never have been awarded. Scientific evidence of that fact is so plentiful and so available that only one conclusion can be drawn: The awarding of the leases constitutes dereliction in the performance of duty by scores of public officials, high and low.

Government does not stand indicted alone. The oil industry must share the guilt, but perhaps in a different way. Members of the industry knew that exploitation of the channel would probably lead to ecological disaster. But they set aside that information in the interest of private gain. It may be somewhat unrealistic to expect private corporations to sacrifice profits for the public good, but the fact that the oil industry chose to ignore strong indications of pending disaster cannot be forgiven. And the fact that the federal government did little in some areas and was powerless in others has grave implications for the American people.

Neither government nor industry can plead innocent by reason of ignorance. California had permitted oil exploration and extraction in the state tidelands of the channel for nearly a decade by the time the federal government awarded its channel leases. None of the state leases was in the immediate vicinity of Santa Barbara, but by the time Platform A went up, there were eight platforms in the state tidelands outside of the Santa Barbara sanctuary. There had been no serious pollution problems from any of the state operations, but undoubtedly there were many near-misses. As one engineer later admitted, "We were just damn lucky."

A tremendous amount of material was collected during the state operations, and most of this information was made available to the federal government. The oil industry, of course, knew the facts clearly. Nearly a year after the blowout, the federal government finally released some of that information in the form of Geological Survey Professional Paper 679, a highly technical research paper entitled "Geology, Petroleum Development, and Seismicity of the Santa Barbara Channel Region, California."

Briefly, the shocking report states: The floor of the channel is highly unstable and poorly equipped to resist leakage. Dozens of earthquake faults rip through the channel, and slippage along the faults is common. Oil reservoirs lie so close to the surface and are covered by earthen material so porous and permeable that leakage is a virtual certainty. While Platform A was being emplaced one of the legs actually pierced a shallow reservoir and oil and gas were bubbling to the surface when workmen were trying to erect the platform. The floor of the channel is so unstable that the oil field is unique among those in California, and perhaps in the entire world.

Seamen who plied the waters of the channel more than a century earlier would not have been surprised by the report —although it probably would have seemed superfluous. The Santa Barbara Channel was well known to mariners of yesteryear, not just because of its natural beauty, dense fogs, and brisk winds, but because of the thin layer of oil that frequently blanketed wide areas of the channel.

The Santa Barbara coastline runs east and west. About twelve miles west of the city, the coastline juts out into the channel, forming a point that has been known for years as Coal Oil Point. Just off the point, oil has been seeping into the channel for centuries. Shipping logs dating back to the middle of the last century mention the oil. There were times when the oil slick from the seepage measured fifty miles long.

The seepage was so dependable that it was used as an aid to navigation. *Sailing Directions for the West Coast of North America, Part 1,* published in London in 1868 by J. F. Imray and Son, informed navigators that when they reached an area where the water was covered by a thin film of oil they probably were approaching the Santa Barbara Mission.

If modern petroleum engineers had been able to tell those old men of the sea that they were going to drill oil wells in the channel, they probably would have been told that the wells would leak.

There were other natural seeps in the channel, including one located beneath Tract 402, where Union Oil Company erected Platform A. Shortly after Union won that lease—and nearly a year before the platform was erected—oil began leaking into the channel near the platform site. Union immediately notified D. W. Solanas, regional oil and gas supervisor for the Conservation Division of the Geological Survey.

In a letter dated February 29, 1968, eleven months prior to the blowout, Union told Solanas that observations had confirmed "a fairly large oil slick with some gas bubbles" near the site of the platform. "From all indications and records available to us, this is apparently a natural seep," the letter stated.

Later, three core holes were drilled in the vicinity of the site for Platform A. The holes were drilled in order to give geologists and petroleum engineers a sample of the strata beneath the channel. According to the Geological Survey report, technicians "observed live oil shows while drilling and coring all three holes at site A, and subsequently reported these findings along with descriptions of oil-saturated core samples and measurements of bulk densities indicative of very high porosities for these oily shallow beds."

Still later, when pilings were being driven for the foundation of the platform, oil and gas were found just below the surface, "and gas was bubbling from the ocean while the platform was being emplaced," the report states.

To grasp the importance of this it is necessary to understand the geological nature of the Santa Barbara Channel, and the nature of oil deposits in general. Most people, when they think of oil in the ground, envision huge cavities in the earth filled with oil. That is a myth. Oil reservoirs are not "reservoirs" at all in the common meaning of the word. When oil is found in the earth it is found in oil-bearing rocks, or oil-bearing strata—frequently layers of sand. The oil occurs because hydrocarbon deposits were trapped in porous rocks or layers of sand eons ago. As the years passed the earth added more layers to its surface. When the layers were impermeable enough to keep the hydrocarbons from forcing their way to the surface, oil was formed and trapped in the "reservoirs." It is there now because the impermeable layers of harder rocks have kept it there despite the tremendous pressures built up over the years during the formation of natural gas. That is why when oil is found it is usually beneath layers of hard rock, sometimes several thousand feet deep, called a "capping layer."

Whether or not it is economically profitable to exploit the reservoirs depends on several factors. The simplest of these is the nature and depth of the capping layer. Geologists believe that vast deposits of oil lie far beneath the surface of the earth, but so far it has not been worth the cost to drill through twenty thousand or thirty thousand feet of extremely hard rock to tap the reserviors. As drilling techniques and equipment improve, and the need grows, it may become worthwhile to exploit those deposits.

The other factors depend upon the oil itself, and the nature of the rocks or sand in which it is found. Oil is found, for example, in solid rocks—such as shale—mixed with other minerals. It is possible to separate the oil from the other minerals, but so far that has proven extremely expensive. Again, as the techniques improve and the demand grows, that, too, may become worthwhile.

The exploitation of oil reserves today depends primarily upon three things: the ease and rapidity with which the oil or gas moves through a sequence of granular rocks (known as the "porosity" of the rocks); the resistance of the oil to flow, known as its "viscosity"; and the pressure within the reservoir itself. Of these, perhaps the most important is the porosity of the rocks. Any student of physics knows that there is open space—though sometimes microscopic in size —in any substance, even the hardest of rocks. However, the size of the open spaces (pores) varies with the nature of the substance.

Generally, finer-grained rocks, such as granite, have smaller pores than coarser-grained rocks, such as sandstone. That is why it is so much harder for liquid (oil) to move through granite than through sandstone.

Thus ideal oil deposits are found under extreme pressure in highly porous rocks or sand, protected by a capping layer that is strong enough to protect the reservoir but shallow enough to allow profitable exploitation of the reservoir.

When oil industry geologists first began eyeing the Santa Barbara Channel they found ample evidence that the oil field complied beautifully with the first two requirements. Sandstone is the basic nature of the Southern California coastline, and its offshore islands, so it was no surprise when the geologists learned that the most common rock formation beneath the channel was sandstone. That meant that the oil deposits probably would be exploitable, at least from a porosity standpoint. Exploratory wells soon demonstrated that the oil deposits were under considerable pressure, as the geologists had expected. But there were some surprises when it came to the capping layer.

Normally, there is no problem with the capping layer unless it is so thick that it rules out the exploitation of the oil field. Rarely is the layer so weak or so fragmented that there is serious danger of fracturing the layer and lowering the pressure in the reservoir—or, in the case of the Santa Barbara Channel, actually releasing the oil into the water. Nature had tested the capping layer time and time again. If the layer had not been strong enough to withstand the passage of time, the pressurized hydrocarbon deposits would have made their way to the surface long ago. The fact that the oil was still there was a good sign that the capping layer was adequate.

But when drillers produced their first core samples, geologists found some surprises. Sure, there was oil beneath the surface. And sure, there was a capping layer. But surprisingly enough, the capping layer was not the highly resistant shield that had been expected. In many cases, the first four hundred or five hundred feet beneath the channel were comprised of siltstone and claystone, interbedded with thin beds of sandstone. Beneath Platform A, layers of sandstone no more than thirty feet below the floor of the channel contained oil, protected by a thin layer of easily fractured siltstone and claystone. It was also found that the first three thousand feet in the Dos Cuadras oil field, where Platform A was located, was composed mostly of sandstone interbedded with thin layers of siltstone, claystone, and shale.

Geological Survey Professional Paper 679 noted that coring samples indicated "that the capping rocks (above five hundred feet deep) at Platform A are not unlike the silty oil sands at greater depths in their range of porosities and permeabilities."

What all of this meant was that the oil deposits were not well protected by a strong capping layer at all—a fact that was corroborated by the channel's long history of natural seeps.

There are other factors that are important here. Four other wells had been drilled from Platform A prior to the blowout of well A-21, wich was the fifth well drilled from the platform. The Geological Survey report notes that in each of the first four wells, "the lost circulation of drilling fluid caused difficulties." At around a depth of two hundred feet, the report states, the drilling mud simply flowed away from the shaft through porous strata instead of back up the shaft the way it was supposed to flow.

"This repeated loss of circulation indicated qualitatively that some part or parts of the capping strata above the shallowest major reservoir of the Dos Cuadras field were permeable to drilling fluid and cement," or simply broke under the pressure of the fluid, the paper notes.

In other words, the capping layer was so weak or porous in some areas that the thick drilling mud simply oozed away. It is little wonder that when the oil reservoirs were finally tapped the oil flowed freely through the capping layer and into the sea through fractures in the rocks.

It is known now—and it should have been known then —that the huge oil reservoirs beneath the Santa Barbara Channel were under intense pressure and in a highly vulnerable setting. The Geological Survey report put it this way: "The fluids in such a large composite accumulation must have been in a delicate, metastable equilibrium, and any drastic uncontrolled disturbance of this balance could result in far-reaching consequences. The blowout of well A-21 triggered such a disturbance."

Oil in subsurface reservoirs generally is accompanied by various gases under high pressure. The report explained what happens when that pressure is suddenly reduced:

"A solution of crude oil and 'gases' is a relatively compressible fluid. It has a strong tendency to expand and to become less dense and more buoyant as the pressure confining it in an underground reservoir rock is reduced. The explosive violence of many well blowouts is attributable to uncontrolled expansion of solution gas resulting from sudden accidental lowering of the pressure in a well bore."

When well A-21 blew out, the sudden lowering of pressure at the bottom of the shaft set off a chain reaction that amounted to a series of explosions far beneath the channel floor. The explosions ripped through the floor with demonic fury, belching out chunks of rocks, some of which were a foot or more across, and leaving large craters throughout the area. The delicate balance of nature had been violated, and the response had been both immediate and devastating.

The blowout at Platform A is now a part of the past: It is "Exhibit A" in the people's case against their government and the oil industry; but it belongs to history. What, now, of the future? What will happen if the drilling continues?

The Geological Survey report had some disturbing observations on the future as well as the past.

Perhaps most troubling is the problem of "subsidence potential." When oil is removed gradually, pressure in the reservoir is lowered. Stated simply, if the pressure is lowered enough, the oil and gas may not be able to support the rocks above the reservoir. The rocks sink slightly, and in some cases the ground far above the reservoir may sink too. This is known as subsidence.

Subsidence probably has been common to oil operations throughout history, but only in recent years has it posed significant problems. It mattered little, for example, if a field on a Texas plain subsided slightly, although nearby farmers may have wondered what made their plaster crack. Where subsidence really matters is along the coast. The classic example is Long Beach, where civic officials became alarmed when they noticed that the tide was lapping higher along their shores, and seaboard buildings that had been high and dry were partly inundated by the waters of the Pacific Ocean. What had happened, of course, is that the ground on which the buildings were built had gradually subsided as oil was extracted from beneath the city, and the buildings slowly sank toward the surf. In some cases, subsidence totaled nearly thirty feet, but the city fathers of Long Beach brought the problem under control before their city threatened to slip into the sea.

After considerable expenditures from public funds, subsidence was largely arrested by pumping water into the reservoirs. In effect, the water replaced the oil and gas, helping to maintain the status quo of the pressures beneath the ground. The water, which was denser than the oil, sank to the bottom of the reservoir, so it was still possible to remove the oil and gas without pumping out the water, too.

And on that point the oil industry got a tremendous bonus. Since the water injections helped maintain the pressure in the reservoir, it was possible to recover far more of the oil than had been expected.

The problem of subsidence in offshore operations is not as neat, however. No one can say for certain that subsidence will occur in the Santa Barbara Channel, but there is no reason to think that it will not occur. It probably will, and when it does, the results could be disastrous. The Geological Survey report noted that subsidence in the channel could cause the inadequate capping layer to fracture, possibly releasing oil and gas into the channel.

"The possibility must be considered that withdrawal of fluids from the reservoirs of the Dos Cuadras oil field may be accompanied and followed by shallow subsurface readjustments and localized subsidence of the sea floor. The exceptionally shallow depth of much of the reservoir volume, the very high porosities and permeabilities of the reservoir rocks, the imperfect caprock seal above the shallowest major reservoir, and the intentional reduction of reservoir pressures, particularly in the shallowest reservoirs, all suggest that fluid withdrawals may be accompanied by reduction of pore [reservoir] pressure and gradual compaction of the petroliferous rocks.

"If compaction occurs," the report continues, "readjustments of the demonstrably weak capping stratum would follow," possibly fracturing the capping layer.

The report noted that water injection "may be feasible and prove effective in maintaining reservoir pressures" more than fourteen hundred feet below the channel floor beneath Platform A. But it pointed out that "water injection into reservoirs [above fourteen hundred feet] must be pursued with great care and forethought to avoid upsetting the delicate pressure balance. The risks unavoidably entailed in shallow injection may prove to be so undesirable that the risks of differential deformation of the capping layer and the sea floor will be regarded as preferable." In other words, it may be possible to reduce subsidence by pumping water into deep reservoirs, but shallow reservoirs are so unstable that it may be better just to pump the oil out and let nature take its course.

The capping layer above the shallow reservoirs was fractured by the blowout, and has been allowing oil and gas to escape ever since. Prior to the issuance of the Geological Survey report, it had been hoped that removal of oil from the shallow reservoirs would reduce the pressure and stop the seepage. But the report revealed that it was not that simple. If the pressure was maintained, the seepage would continue. If the pressure was lowered through the extraction of oil, subsidence could fracture the caprock, thus allowing even more oil and gas to escape into the channel. It all added up to a hell of a predicament for the oil industry, the government, and especially for the people of Southern California.

Suppose, for the sake of argument, that this "damned if they do and damned if they don't" predicament worked out for the best. What if during the next two or three decades oil is removed from the channel, subsidence poses no serious problems, and no one makes any mistakes? Is there sound reason to believe that if everything works out better than we have reason to expect, there will be no further contamination?

That question can be answered in one word. No. There is no such chance. If the channel is to be exploited, and it appears now that it will, then major contamination is a virtual certainty. Oil industry executives who testified in congressional hearings repeatedly refused to assure the people that there would be no more disasters in the channel. They knew the odds were stacked against them.

California is earthquake country, a fact which has been demonstrated on a disturbingly regular basis. On February 9, 1971, a quake of magnitude 6.5 on the Richter Scale ripped through the northwestern suburbs of Los Angeles, destroying four hospitals. One of the hospitals was only a month old. Two three-and-four-story buildings at a Veterans Administration hospital in suburban Sylmar collapsed, killing or fatally injuring forty-five persons and trapping scores of others inside the wreckage. A new freeway bridge which had been designed with earthquakes in mind collapsed onto a pickup truck and killed two men. A total of sixty-four persons died in the quake, another reminder of man's frailty and nature's power.

The Santa Barbara Channel is perhaps one of the last places in the world where offshore production should have been permitted. At least thirty or forty faults (weaknesses in the earth's crust along which movement occurs during a quake) knife through the floor of the channel. Most are concentrated in the area where the federal government awarded its leases. Indeed, one of the faults passes within a few feet of Platform A and actually intersects well A-21.

Since 1912, more than twenty earthquakes of magnitude 6.0 or larger on the Richter Scale have occurred in Southern California. A temblor of magnitude 6.0 is capable of causing considerable structural damage. Two of those twenty quakes occurred within the Santa Barbara Channel, and a third— measuring 7.5—struck in the Pacific in 1927 west of Point Arguello, just beyond the northern mouth of the channel about fifty miles from Santa Barbara.

The Geological Survey report cites four earthquakes that were especially destructive in the Santa Barbara area. The report states:

The earliest, in 1812, destroyed Missions Santa Barbara and Purisima Conception [about ten miles northeast of Point Arguello] and caused a tsunami [a sea wave created by an earthquake] along the north coast of the channel. Reported estimates of the high-water mark of this tsunami were as much as fifty feet. A recent detailed study of historic records, however, concludes that such accounts are unsubstantiated and cannot be accepted at face value. Several asphalt [crude oil] springs reportedly began to flow at places inland from the coast, and a burning oil spring near Rincon Point [south of Santa Barbara] was enlarged. The reported damage and other effects resemble those accompanying other California earthquakes of magnitude 7.

An earthquake on June 29, 1925, caused widespread damage in coastal communities from Pismo Beach on the northwest, through Santa Barbara, to Ventura on the east. Twenty people were killed. Almost the entire business section of Santa Barbara was destroyed or rendered unsafe. The damage was estimated at six million dollars, and this figure does not include damage to residences. Mission Santa Barbara again was heavily damaged with partial destruction of two bell towers, collapse of the front façade, and failure of some older interior adobe walls. [Seismologist Herbert] Nunn (1925) reports that crude oil was extruded through beach sand at several points along the Santa Barbara coast about three hours before the main earthquake and at approximately the same time as a series of slight foreshocks began. An oil spout also was observed at the shoreline near the west end of the present Summerland oil field one night after an earthquake in 1883. The epicenter of this magnitude 6.3 earthquake was probably less than ten miles southwest of Santa Barbara.

The third major earthquake occurred on November 11, 1927, northwest of the channel off Point Arguello. This shock, with a magnitude of 7.5, ranks as the second-largest California earthquake since the San Francisco earthquake of 1906. Effects were most pronounced at Surf and Honda, just north of Point Arguello, where people were thrown from their beds, the concrete highway was cracked, a railroad bridge was damaged, and several hundred thousand cubic feet of sand were shaken down from a beach cliff. Buildings were damaged along the coast from Cambria, about eighty miles northwest of Point Arguello, to Gaviota, twenty-eight miles to the east. A seismic sea wave was generated by the main event, and seismic disturbances from the main shock and some of its stronger aftershocks were felt in ships at sea. The seismic sea wave, or tsunami, was observed at Surf and Pismo Beach, ten and forty miles, respectively, north of Point Arguello. The wave was at least six feet high and resembled a large storm wave. At Port

San Luis near Pismo Beach, a five-foot wave was followed by one hour of water agitation. Tide gauge records at San Francisco and San Diego confirm this tsunami.

The last of the four important earthquakes occurred on June 30, 1941. Its magnitude was 5.9-6.0 and its epicenter was located in the channel about five miles south of the coastline between Santa Barbara and Carpinteria. Several communities along the Santa Barbara coast were damaged.

In addition to these major temblors, consistent seismic activity of a lesser magnitude has occurred in the channel. Frequently this has consisted of a series of small shakes called "earthquake swarms."

There is, of course, far more to an earthquake than its magnitude. Damage to manmade structures depends largely upon the type of structure, and the nature of the ground upon which it was built. The old biblical analogy is as accurate here as it was in the past. A house built upon a rock will stand, but a house built upon shifting sands will fall. That is true here simply because the rock does not move as much as the sands. The Geological Survey report described it like this:

"Although field experimental data that bear on ground amplification [the strength of the seismic wave as it moves through the ground] are sparse, research has been done on seismic waves generated by underground nuclear explosions in Nevada and recorded in the San Francisco Bay region. Ground-motion amplitudes recorded on soils and sediments near the margins of the bay were compared with those recorded on nearby bedrock outcrops. Maximum amplifications were observed on thick sections of 'younger Bay mud' near the margins of the bay. At such sites, the peak ground-motion velocities were as much as ten times larger than on nearby bedrock sites; and corresponding peak values in the ratio of the Fourier spectra [which reflect the duration and amplitude of shaking] were as much as thirty times larger than those observed on bedrock. This means that the amount of power or energy that is dissipated at a given frequency can be as much as thirty times greater on unconsolidated sediments than on bedrock.

"It is probable that soft sediments in the Santa Barbara Channel region would also suffer such amplified shaking," the report states.

The effect of an earthquake upon the gargantuan towers erected on the sandstone of the Santa Barbara Channel could be total. Although no one can say that a major quake would tumble all the towers, there is no reason to believe that such a quake would not cause severe damage and probable leakage.

Seismic damage to oil-field installations in California has been verified again and again. Storage tanks have been destroyed, oil and gas pipelines ruptured, and subsurface installations damaged.

What does all of this say about the future? Will there be more major quakes? If so, will the quakes lead to further contamination?

Accurate earthquake predictors are hard to come by these days, but there is ample evidence that the Santa Barbara Channel will shake for some time to come. Seismologists have theorized that an earthquake of 8.0 should occur once every fifty-two years. If their predictions come true, the great temblor that Southern California has been expecting for years is already past due.

"Such a great earthquake anywhere in Southern California probably would have destructive effects in the Santa Barbara Channel region," the Geological Survey report states. "Its aftershocks, many of which also would be destructive, might be expected to occur over an area the size of Southern California."

It is interesting to note that the report contends that two earthquakes in recent history were caused by oil field operations.

"Fluid injection seems to have caused earthquakes in at least two places. [The fluid was injected in an effort to maintain pressures in the reservoir, thus making it possible to extract more of the oil, known as "secondary recovery."] The injection of water into a twelve-thousand-foot-deep well at the Rocky Mountain Arsenal northeast of Denver, Colorado is generally considered to have initiated the earthquake sequence that began there in 1962. Three of these earthquakes had magnitudes of greater than 5 and resulted in minor damage. The probable cause of the earthquakes was weakening of rock through increased pore pressure, which allowed natural rock stresses to be released. Another situation that possibly is similar to that in Denver was subsequently recognized in the oil field near Rangely, Colorado. The earthquakes there occurred in areas of high-pressure gradients generated by injection of water for purposes of secondary recovery."

The report tends generally to play down the effect of earthquakes on oil operations in the Santa Barbara Channel, contending that most of the hazards could be circumvented by sound engineering. The report claims, for example, that if the towers were destroyed by a quake it would cause only "minor danger to the environment unless wells are at critical stages of drilling or development. Completed wells have chokes and automatic cutoff valves at the sea floor. It is noteworthy that platforms have been destroyed by gulf coast hurricanes and have not resulted in significant oil spills."

The report also suggests:

Ruptures in oil lines would release only "limited" amounts of oil, since the pipelines are equipped with automatic shut-off valves. Storage tanks onshore can be designed to withstand earthquakes. Damage to the wells themselves probably would not lead to contamination, since in the past, earth movement has "pinched off" wells, thus inhibiting leakage rather than causing it.

Those assurances offer little comfort to people who have watched the oil operations in the channel. On December 16, 1969, nearly a year after the blowout at Platform A, a pipeline leading from the platform to the shore ruptured in the middle of the night. It spewed oil into the water throughout the night, and oil once again washed up on the shores of the channel. The automatic shutoff device did not work.

Even if the shutoff devices function according to plan, contamination is still possible. John L. Wiester, a Santa Barbara resident representing anti-oil forces, testified before the Senate subcommittee on minerals, materials, and fuels on July 21–22, 1970. He said, in part:

"The present Union Oil Company pipeline contains 7675 barrels of oil and the Phillips Petroleum Company [the only other company producing at that time] pipeline carries 3090 barrels of oil for a total of 10,765 barrels. If the channel is fully developed, the possibility exists of a spill from this source of 100,000 barrels, from which it would take decades to recover."

All this material points to one inescapable fact. Regardless of attempts by the federal government and the oil industry to distort the evidence, the threat of massive contamination from oil operations as a result of earthquakes is real indeed. It is interesting to note the reaction of oil industry executives to this danger. They have suggested repeatedly that the industry actually may be doing the people a favor. Their reasoning is mystifying. On the one hand they claim earthquakes pose no real danger to oil field operations, but then they turn around and suggest that quakes could rupture the channel floor, even if oil operations were not under way, and spill the oil into the channel. To hear them tell it, they may be saving the environment by getting the oil out before mother nature belches it into the sea of her own free will. If their reasoning is accurate, one wonders why she has waited so long.

Aside from natural calamity, there is another danger that will exist as long as oil operations are under way in the Santa Barbara Channel, and in any coastal waters, for that matter. It is the danger of a collision. The channel is one of the major sea lanes on the West Coast. On this point, it is worthwhile to quote the entire testimony of Santa Barbara resident Donald L. McFarland, who appeared before the U. S. Senate subcommittee on minerals, materials, and fuels in Santa Barbara on March 15, 1970:

It is a matter of Coast Guard record that on Saturday, October 19, 1968, I departed Santa Barbara Harbor on a sailboat race to Santa Cruz Island. A dense fog set in around noon and by 3 P.M. the race was called for lack of wind. In about one-hundred-foot visibility, I proceeded under power to the island, periodically sounding my fog horn. A short time later, I saw a cable rising diagonally out of the water a few boat lengths ahead. I swung the boat violently and narrowly missed being dismasted. Having altered course, I idled the motor and listened for a fog horn or any evidence of a tug boat with a tow. All I could hear were machinery noises and metallic clanking. I had nearly collided with the newly installed Platform A, which had no warning devices in operation. I cannot help but observe that this careless disregard for safety was subsequently to be dramatized by the blowout on the following January 28.

On June 16, 1968, a 492-foot freighter was heading south through the fog-bound channel while an Alaska-bound Navy tanker loaded with five million gallons of jet fuel was feeling her way north. Despite all modern direction-finding and warning devices, they met head-on in the middle of a two-mile buffer zone separating the mile-wide passing lanes. To make matters worse, the vessels apparently were not certain where they were—reporting their positions to Coast Guard [as] twenty-four miles from the scene of the collision.

These shipping lanes are known to local yachtsmen as "wind alley." They are subject to heavy and prolonged fogs in addition to the huge swells caused by the wind streaming off Point Conception. They pass directly through approximately two dozen oil lease areas.

In early October 1969, the Army Corps of Engineers approved exploratory drilling on three parcels, two of which are in the northbound shipping lane in the Point Conception "graveyard of ships" area. Just two months later, on December 5, 1969, the Matson passenger liner *Lurline* was proceeding north under a clear night sky when she was forced to alter course to avoid collision with the drilling barge *Bluewater II*. In a Notice to Mariners, the Coast Guard reports that "the anchoring system for these vessels may extend to five thousand feet from the vessel. The limits of the anchoring system are marked by orange and white vertically striped buoys equipped with white lights flashing every two seconds. Mariners should not pass between these buoys and the drilling vessel." In other words, by Coast Guard definition, navigation is hazardous for a two-mile diameter around a drilling barge. Yet drilling permits are granted for areas inside a one-mile-wide shipping lane!

The problems of unlighted buoys randomly clustered around drilling platforms are all too well known to local yachtsmen and fishermen. A Morro Bay couple found themselves in the water off Goleta after ramming an unlighted platform buoy. No trace of their boat was found although they were rescued by the Coast Guard. Despite such incidents and numerous complaints from boat operators, such buoys remain unlighted.

Although small-boat traffic in the channel poses no disaster threat except to the unfortunate crew, the vision of three-hundred-thousand-ton supertankers coming down from Alaska and threading their way through the oil platforms and drilling barges, soon to populate the Santa Barbara Channel, is enough to give the citizens of Southern California nightmares. Our January 28 blowout would be a tea party compared to the results of a collision between a sixty-well platform and a supertanker. The oil industry says it can't happen—with modern navigation aids and safety devices on the platforms. But we in Santa Barbara are all too familiar with things that can't happen, starting with the January 28 disaster. Since that time, Sun Oil's highly touted superplatform turned upside down and sank while attempting to maneuver into position. A large pipeline cracked on Platform A, spilling heavily into the ocean for many hours before it was discovered. The safety devices and automatic shutoffs so heavily publicized simply didn't work.

I believe we are justifiably skeptical of the oil industries' assurances—and when faced with the collision of a U. S. Navy-operated vessel with a freighter in the lease area, we can only conclude that continued development of the federal oil leases will inevitably lead to a disaster of epic proportions.

All of these facts underscore the point that leases in the channel should not have been awarded. But by the time this information trickled down to the public, it was too late. The leases had been sold, oil operations were under way, and there was virtually no chance of reversing that situation. And there was no chance that offshore production could be carried out without pollution.

Finally, the Department of the Interior, in a move aimed more at placating seacoast residents than resolving the problem, issued tighter regulations for offshore operations following the blowout. Among the new requirements: Companies drilling on offshore leases would be absolutely liable for pollution.

The new regulations brought the usual outcry of righteous indignation from the oil industry, but the most surprising and revealing response came from a small Los Angeles-based company, Pauley Petroleum, Inc. Pauley was the operator for, and a member of, a group of eleven oil companies that purchased two leases in the channel. The other companies were Ashland Oil, Inc.; Colorado Oil and Gas Corporation; Mesa Petroleum Company; McCulloch Oil Corporation; J. M. Huber Corporation; Husky Oil Company of Delaware; Midwest Oil Corporation; Kewanee Oil Company; Macdonald Oil Corporation, and Forest Oil Corporation.

In behalf of all eleven companies, Pauley filed a 230-million-dollar lawsuit against the federal government, charging that the new regulations virtually negated the lease. The suit claimed that: 1) the U.S. government knew, or should have known, when it asked for bids, that the parcels were

in deep water and in known fault areas that were subjected
to earthquakes and tsunamis; 2) drilling on the leases in
the channel required operations that reached the known
limits of relevant technology; 3) the leases were in a channel
heavily traveled by ships, thus increasing the chances of
pollution.

The suit is expected to be tied up in the courts for several
years. What the suit said, in effect, was that the government had every reason to expect pollution at the time it
awarded the leases and that it was unfair to change the
rules of the game when everyone knew there was only one
way the game could be played—dirty.

4

The general feeling throughout Santa Barbara in the winter of 1968–69 had been one of resignation. The people had tried to keep the oil industry out, but they had failed. The industry had paid more than 602 million dollars for the leases in the channel, and by the time January 1969 rolled around expensive platforms had been erected. There would be no turning back, or so nearly everyone thought. One exception was Alvin C. Weingand, a former Democratic state senator. Weingand, a man of small physical stature who knows the ways of politics, had long fought to make the Channel Islands a national monument, preserving the integrity of the islands for generations to come, and he felt deeply about the channel.

When oil began leaking into the water beneath Platform A, Weingand was one of the first to recognize that this would not be just another oil spill. As a long-time resident of Santa Barbara, he knew his channel well, and he sensed that something was terribly wrong. And as a veteran politician, he had reason to doubt the reassurances from the oil industry.

Weingand first heard of the blowout from two friends, James "Bud" Bottoms, a commercial artist, and Marvin Stuart, a public relations man.

"They called me and said, 'We have had a terrible calamity that is going to be the ruination of this area,'" Weingand recalled later. "I said, 'My God, what should we do?'"

Bottoms and Stuart had a plan. They knew that many

Santa Barbarans would not know what to do, and both men felt it would be important to give them an outlet. They decided to form an organization that would serve as a catch basin for ideas and anti-oil programs. And they thought immediately of Al Weingand. Nearly two years earlier, Weingand had led a fight that netted a major victory for the thinking people of Santa Barbara. At that time, the county Board of Supervisors had authorized Humble Oil and Refining Company to build a processing plant on the shore several miles east of Santa Barbara. Within about two weeks, residents collected ten thousand signatures calling for a referendum. The board's action was rescinded by the voters. But everyone knew that success would not come that quickly again.

The first move of the new three-man organization was to begin contacting people they knew they could trust. And in keeping with the political style of the day, they also called a rally.

One of the first people they called was Mrs. Lois Sidenberg, who had moved to Santa Barbara in 1947 with her husband, George, a Navy pilot turned stockbroker. Mrs. Sidenberg, who had always considered organization women "bloody bores," turned to organizations herself after her husband died in 1956. She joined the League of Women Voters and several other groups, and soon developed a knack for getting things done.

Scores of people were notified of the rally, and on Monday, February 3, nearly a week after the blowout, thousands of people gathered on the beach. The crowd included people from all walks of life, every political persuasion, and differing economic and social backgrounds. But they all had one thing in common: desperation.

The tone of the rally was perhaps best revealed by a little old lady in her nineties who listened quietly as Weingand asked toward the end of the rally if anyone from the oil industry was present and wanted to make a statement.

"If there is," the elderly woman whispered to Mrs. Sidenberg, "I will kill them."

By the time the rally had ended, one thing was evident: The blowout at Platform A had united the people of Santa Barbara as had no other issue in the history of the city. Campus dissidents from nearby Santa Barbara campus of the University of California were united with political chieftains and business executives; Democrats joined with Republicans; the rich stood beside the poor, the old with the young. Under Weingand's direction, the course was set: They would work within the system; there would be no insurrection, no violence; they would depend upon their elected officials to make the right decisions, but they would not let anyone forget what had happened in Santa Barbara.

And so it was that the fight to save Santa Barbara was born, perhaps too late, imbued with the conviction that the system could be made to work. But even the most seasoned politicos soon were forced to admit that the blowout and the subsequent fight told them things about their system that they did not want to believe.

Out of that early rally grew an organization that may have done more than its share in reshaping the direction of American life. The organization was named "Get Oil Out!" (GOO!) and it became a model for similar programs across the nation. From the beginning, GOO! involved a wide spectrum of people.

School children who had always thought of the beach as a sandy, sunny place to have fun, gathered in February following the blowout for a different purpose. The kids moved solemnly along the beach as they collected samples of crude oil in bottles. Later, they labeled the bottles, jotted down a few observations, and sent the samples to state legislators.

That same month, GOO! officially opened its office in a small building in downtown Santa Barbara. The office was staffed by volunteers wearing black armbands.

The organization sponsored art exhibits featuring paintings and photographs of the oil spill. A melodrama sponsored by GOO! lampooned the oil industry in "Fair Barbara's Fault" or "Oil's Well that Ends Well."

Santa Barbara's plight was picked up and carried around the world by news media. The usually staid, conservative Santa Barbara *News-Press* made the oil spill its top issue of the decade, denouncing the oil industry and the government in strong terms. Farther south, the Los Angeles *Times,* by far the largest and most influential newspaper in western America, joined the fight as it editorialized for an end to drilling in the channel.

GOO!'s formula for success was basic: Keep as many people involved as possible; use all resources wisely; and *make* news instead of waiting for it to happen.

There was something for everyone in the program. Experts in various fields were called upon to use their expertise, including such things as geology, biology, and politics. State and national leaders were attracted to Santa Barbara— in some cases almost at the end of a rope—to see the problem firsthand. In addition to winning converts, the stream of powerful figures provided a constant flow of news stories carrying the dateline of Santa Barbara. The visiting bigshots ranged from legislators to the President of the United States, Richard Nixon. Unfortunately, by the time Nixon arrived in late March the beaches of Santa Barbara literally had been sand blasted and steam cleaned.

Meanwhile, volunteers fanned out over Southern California with petitions calling for a halt to oil operations in the channel. Within four months, more than one hundred thousand persons had signed the petitions, which were delivered personally to Washington by GOO! representatives. Twenty-one organizations and various city and county officers added their own statements to the petitions, all of which were virtually ignored. By early 1970, the number of signatures on the petitions had climbed to over two hundred thousand. An attempt to deliver the petitions to the President while he was at his "White House" in San Clemente the following January was thwarted by presidential aides.

During the long months following the blowout, GOO! representatives appeared frequently before congressional committees. But unlike the hysterical presentations that are typical of novice political organizations, GOO! consistently put its best foot forward, calling upon experts to testify within their fields and constantly offering logic and reason in the face of hostility.

Initially, GOO! operated on a thirty-five-hundred-dollar monthly budget, although that figure was reduced more than a year after the spill to around fifteen hundred dollars. The money came from contributors across the nation—one woman in Michigan faithfully sent her dividend check from oil stocks every month. Occasionally, a large check would come in, sometimes up to one thousand dollars, but usually the gifts reflected the nature of the organization: a little help from a lot of people.

As the months passed, GOO! won some battles and lost others, and the effort emerged partly as a lesson in frustration. "I have always thought that I understood how our system worked," said Mrs. Sidenberg as she reflected one day on the long battle. "But this has been a shock."

She recalled that when Secretary of the Interior Walter Hickel arrived in Santa Barbara during the spill, he met for several hours with oil company executives at a plush hotel. No one else was permitted to attend.

"So I called later and said I wanted a copy of the minutes of the meeting. I was told no one kept minutes. I said 'You mean to tell me that a public official met with members of private industry and no one kept minutes?' I couldn't believe it!"

That pattern continued to dominate the long fight between the people of Santa Barbara, the government, and the oil industry. During the fight, all too many officials demonstrated that they were either controlled by, or so sympathetic with, the oil industry that they were unable to protect the public interest. One of the best examples is Donald W. Solanas, regional supervisor of oil and gas operations for the U. S. Geological Survey.

Solanas is not just another bureaucrat. As the man who is most responsible for watching the industry and enforcing federal regulations on oil operations, he was the public's watchdog. It was his job to see, among other things, that the channel was not polluted through unsafe operations. He had the opportunity several times to act, especially when Union Oil Company notified him on two occasions prior to the blowout that oil was seeping into the channel on Tract 402—once shortly after the lease was signed, and again when Platform A was being emplaced.

He admitted during a congressional hearing that he had not even been on the platform during the entire time that well A-21 was being drilled, and neither had anyone from his office. He thus saw the well for the first time after it had blown out.

Solanas is a suave, silver-haired man who makes no secret of his affection for the oil industry. He wears a small gold oil derrick as a tiebar, and the curtains in his Los Angeles office are imprinted with derricks. His office serves as a distribution center for the oil industry's literature, much of which has been published by the federal government.

Solanas was—and still is—the people's number one enforcer of regulations governing oil operations on federal leases in California, Oregon, Washington, Nevada, and along the continental shelf of the West Coast. His concern, above all else, should have been to protect the public interest. During one hearing, he kept insisting that requirements placed on Union Oil were more strict than normal. When he was asked what requirements he was referring to, Solanas replied:

"We required Union Oil to have an adequate drilling program and to comply with standard oil field backup procedures."

To that, Senator Joseph Montoya, Democrat of New Mexico, barked:

"I haven't been able to get specific answers to my questions from you. What specifically was done in this case that isn't usually done?"

"Well," Solanas replied, "we encouraged everybody concerned to be more actively mentally alert, to try to maintain more caution in every person's mind."

"You mean the extra precautions were mental and that no additional equipment, for example, was used?" Montoya asked.

"Yes, that's what I meant to say," Solanas answered.

Solanas surfaced on a regular basis as an antagonist in the fight to save the channel. It was largely upon his insistence that the first federal lease in the channel was granted. He argued that wells on state leases "might" be draining oil from pools beneath the federal tidelands, and he said it was thus necessary to exploit the federal reserves in order to save them from being drained off by nearby state wells. His argument was never documented with evidence, but that was not necessary. The oil interests won anyway.

Several months after the blowout, GOO! representatives in small boats tried to block the emplacement of Sun Oil Company's platform by locating their boats in the area where they thought the platform was to be erected. Solanas, riding on a Coast Guard cutter, at one point leaned over the side and shouted to the citizens that he was writing down their names to give to the Justice Department.

Solanas's counterpart in the California state government turned in a similar performance. Immediately after the blowout, the California Lands Commission imposed a moratorium on oil drilling on state-owned lands in the channel. The state also revoked fifteen exploratory drilling permits. Frank J. Hortig, executive officer of the commission, and thus the state's "watchdog," consistently recommended lifting the moratorium and proceeding with oil operations in the state tidelands, claiming that no permanent damage had resulted from the blowout.

Fortunately, the commission chose to ignore Hortig.

Frustration in the fight against the oil industry and the federal government was not limited to the people of Santa Barbara. After the blowout, the state of California joined with the city and county of Santa Barbara in a four-hundred-million-dollar damage suit against Union Oil. The state put the suit in the hands of one its best lawyers, Chief Deputy Attorney General Charles A. O'Brien, a fighting Irishman. In order to prepare the suit, O'Brien needed expert testimony from authorities in the field of petroleum engineering and geology. He turned to universities throughout the state, but ran into roadblocks. During a Santa Barbara luncheon two months after the blowout, O'Brien described what had happened:

"We began contacting petroleum engineering and oil geology experts at universities in California to assist us in preparation of our case," O'Brien said. "So far, we have been unable to procure expert advice.

"It is an old refrain. The university experts all seem to be working on grants from the oil industry. There is an atmosphere of fear. These experts are afraid if they assist us in our case on behalf of the people of California, they will lose their oil industry grants. I find this industry domination of university researchers to be deplorable."

Dr. Lyman L. Handy, chairman of the department of petroleum engineering at the private University of Southern California, admitted that campuses were deeply beholden to oil firms for financial support, but he said "that doesn't mean we have sold out to them." However, when USC conducted an extensive investigation into the Santa Barbara incident under an oil industry grant, most of the information was withheld from the public.

O'Brien was even more infuriated over the role of the University of California at Santa Barbara, a state-supported institution. During a press conference on July 2, 1970, he charged that UC Santa Barbara received a seven-thousand-dollar federal grant from the Department of the Interior for a study of damage to animal and plant life from the oil spill. He said his office tried for a year to get a copy of the study, but the university refused.

"This office [state attorney general] has been repeatedly refused a copy of the study on grounds that the university is under Department of Interior's orders not to release the study until certain parts are changed," O'Brien said. He added that all but one copy of the report had been destroyed.

"Frankly, we're getting a little irritated at the state-supported university accepting federal funds [for studies] and then refusing to make the information available to the public," said O'Brien, who appealed directly to Secretary Hickel for release of the report. In his letter to Hickel, O'Brien said that a news article in the San Francisco *Chronicle* (based on a press release put out by the university, not on the report itself) reported that the study indicated that "heavy biological damage occurred in the intertidal surf grass and barnacle population . . . giant kelp . . . sustained damage" and that "cleaning of the rocks damaged certain organisms."

University officials later said they had planned to release the report on April 22, Earth Day, but that the report was "frozen" because of the Justice Department's involvement in oil spill litigation.

Such maneuvers by the federal government had become standard operational procedures, O'Brien charged that summer.

"Our office's experiences in the Santa Barbara oil suits have distressed everyone connected with the suits in terms of lack of candor and virtual chicanery we have found at federal executive levels."

He cited refusal of the U. S. Geological Survey to permit the state to examine its files, and he accused the Army Corps of Engineers of violating its own regulations requiring consideration of environment when approving an oil drilling platform. When a lawsuit was filed by citizens and the state, he said, "the corps faced the problem boldly—it simply changed its regulations after the [suit was filed] so that it could ignore the environment, and went on its way."

The corps now claims that its only legal justification for denying to issue a permit for a platform is if the platform would constitute a hazard to navigation.

Because of a lack of independent research, the federal government's main source of information was the oil industry itself, O'Brien said, and thus the government knew only what the industry wanted it to know. Even that limited source was withheld on the grounds that the information was "privileged."

During a congressional hearing, O'Brien summed it up like this:

"The federal government appears one day as Mr. Clean, the foe of dirty water. The next day, the same government puts on its black hat and pollutes our waters."

It appeared, he said, that "prior to the Santa Barbara disaster the federal government had planned to sell oil rights the length of the California coast."

"Is this the best way to balance the federal budget?" O'Brien asked. "The California coastline is a unique national asset. Why is its worth diminished by erecting offshore structures the size of twenty-story apartments between the ocean sunset and the people who come to view the sunset?"

It is important to remember that while all of this was going on, oil continued to seep into the channel in varying amounts. Well A-21 was listed officially as under control eleven days after the blowout, but less than a month after the first oil began leaking into the channel a new slick began to form from beneath Platform A. A spokesman for Union Oil Company said the slick—which measured eight miles long within two days—began gurgling to the surface while workmen were preparing to pump from another well on the platform in hopes of relieving pressure beneath the surface of the channel. Experts speculated that the idea to relieve the pressure had backfired. Meanwhile, the slick drifted toward shore, where workmen were still trying to clean up the earlier mess.

Nearly ten months later, another spill blackened the channel, creating a fifty-square-mile slick and washing oil ashore along twenty-two miles of coastline from Santa Barbara to Ventura. It resulted from a pipeline break.

It was impossible, of course, for the oil industry to deny the presence of the slicks, so it did the next best thing: It misled the public as to the quantity of oil leaking into the channel. In fairness, it must be said that it is extremely difficult to gauge the amount of oil in any slick. But the original estimates by Union Oil Company are so contradictory to other reports that the only logical conclusion is that the industry deliberately understated the amount of oil leaking into the channel.

At the time of the blowout, Union insisted that maximum leakage was only about five hundred barrels of oil a day. A subsequent study by the General Research Corporation of Santa Barbara, under contract to the county, disagreed sharply with Union's estimate and suggested that the actual amount was probably at least ten times greater than Union's figure. The study, conducted ten months after the blowout, was based primarily upon examination of a wide range of aerial photographs and subsequent determination, largely through color and characteristics, of the thickness and width of the slick.

Alan A. Allen, one of the authors of the report, emphasized that some degree of error should be tolerated since measuring techniques are far from exact, but one is forced to wonder about the disparity between five hundred and five thousand barrels a day. Geological Survey Professional Paper 679 (*Geology, Petroleum Development, and Seismicity of the Santa Barbara Channel Region, California*) indicates that Allen's estimate may have been too high, but it also indicates that Union's estimate was far too low.

But one is still forced to wonder. Could Union have merely been mistaken? It seems improbable.

Recent surveys of current seepage into the channel around Platform A reveal that the seepage has been reduced to only about ten barrels a day, but it is important to realize that vast quantities of oil are still leaking through the floor of the channel and are not included in that figure.

Several months after the blowout, an underwater "tent city" was lowered to the floor of the channel around Platform A. The tents were the work of Richard R. Headrick, a former child movie star who turned inventor and became a consultant to Firestone Coated Fabrics Company.

The tents are pyramidal in shape and measure one hundred feet square. They are made of nylon fabric covered with polyvinyl chloride. The fabric is attached to a huge frame made out of steel pipe measuring twenty inches in diameter.

In April 1969, the first tent was towed to a site near Platform A. The pipe frame was flooded and the tent sank to the bottom of the channel. A float held the center of the tent up about seventeen feet above the bottom, creating an inverted funnel. A four-inch pipe ran from the peak to the platform. Oil seeping through the channel floor beneath the tent was trapped, along with natural gas. The oil was forced to slide up the underside of the fabric and into the pipe. Expanding natural gas forced the oil up the pipe to the platform, where it was separated from the water and fed into the regular production line.

Since that time, several other tents have been lowered to the bottom of the channel, covering between 70 and 80 percent of the floor around the platform. Although it is true that the tents have prevented a great deal of oil from seeping into the water, they have also provided a false sense of security. The oil industry has sought repeatedly to convince the public that well A-21 is no longer leaking, and all is well beneath Platform A.

The oil industry is a master at convincing the public of whatever it wants the public to believe, and it never hesitates to use its money and its power to influence popular opinion. Several months after the blowout, the industry paid the bills for a national advertising campaign by the Santa Barbara Chamber of Commerce. The intent of the campaign was to convince tourists across the nation that no harm had been done to Santa Barbara by the oil industry. The campaign provoked such outrage from many sectors of the community that for a while the continued existence of the chamber was in doubt.

The industry carried out its own propaganda campaign. More than twenty-one thousand brochures were mailed to influential persons declaring that the "cries for regulation" since the spill "verge on hysteria."

Most regretfully, selected news media also contributed to the spread of false information. The Chamber of Commerce, again with the financial support of the oil industry, imported dozens of reporters from newspapers across the country to tell their side of the story. Unfortunately, the chamber specifically solicited "outdoors" writers, most of whom were not particularly adept at investigative reporting. They returned to their papers and wrote predictable stories.

"I walked the beaches and found globs of crude oil in the sand, but it wasn't bad enough to keep people at home," wrote Tom Foust of the *Arizona Daily Star* in Tucson. "In fact, there are native Santa Barbarans who will tell you that it's not much worse than it has always been from natural seeps. . . . But one thing is sure: The community is taking a bum rap because it's not the oily mess it has been made out to be."

Walt Radke of the San Francisco *Examiner* saw it like this:

"Despite the plaints of bleeding hearts and certain conservation groups, the California Fish and Game Department . . . and this ink-stained wretch are having a tough time tying any honest fish losses to that mammoth oil spill that occurred here January 28."

A number of other "outdoors" writers tossed their lines over the side of a boat, caught a fish, and the world looked rosy.

It is too bad that the Chamber of Commerce did not introduce the visiting writers to David Reed, a commercial fisherman in the waters around Santa Barbara for most of his life. Reed, in a hearing before the House subcommittee on mines and mining in September 1970, told the committee:

"Prior to the oil well blowout of 1969 I was engaged as a fisherman of pelagic fishes, of barracuda, albacore, white sea-bass, tuna, bonita. Since that time I have been unable to make a living fishing for these fishes and have had to start learning a new livelihood."

Reed told the committee that he was forced to turn more to abalone diving in an attempt to earn a living and support his family.

"Before the massive blowout we were able to operate on a strict censure of our own doing, as far as the amount of dozens of abalone that we allowed ourselves to take per day. This was generally from twenty-five to fifty dozen per day. Since the oil well blowout we are lucky to get twenty to fifty dozen abalone per week. Or even every two weeks. Prior to the blowout of January 1969 we were able to harvest our abalone in this area, and other areas, through a system of known growth rate per year, per type of abalone. Then, knowing the location of the abalone beds and the size of those abalone, we could tell within a month one way or another when we could go in and harvest. Just as a farmer can tell when to go in and harvest his crop of corn. Since the big blowout the abalone have ceased to grow at a known rate. It is a completely different setup altogether. We are now forced to get abalone on a catch-as-catch-can basis. The abalone that we know of are still there but they have not grown. For a year or more they have not grown at all. I have found black deposits on the abalone which I consider to be oil, crude oil or detergents mixed with crude oil, at forty- and fifty-foot depths. In some cases these deposits are found even at sixty to sixty-five feet.

"During the time of the big oil spill a year and a half ago, it was closed season for abalone diving in the Santa Barbara Channel. And, as with every fishery, seasons are closed because the abalone are having their young. The young abalone are pelagic in nature—that is, free-swimming creatures that survive for a period of up to two weeks. Then their shells form, causing enough weight to sink them to the bottom where they grow to the size where we may harvest them," Reed testified.

However, in the case of the young, they died on contact with the surface oil, and a complete cycle in the life of the abalone was lost.

"This, of course, is of great concern to us not only as individual abalone divers, but also to our children and our children's children in time to come, as it means there will be a complete break in the cycle of the abalone. There always has been a high mortality rate in the abalone, but with the advent of the oil and of the detergents to sink it, or supposedly to do so, we have had a much greater mortality rate than normal. We have heard many of those connected with the oil companies say that the crude oil released into our ocean has had no effect on, and has not harmed our marine life. This I will have to say from my own experience is not true. It has had a disastrous effect!"

There were other "David Reeds" in Santa Barbara, not all of whom were commercial fishermen. Tourism dropped sharply, due partly to the oil and partly to a general decline in the economy. But the oil industry chose to ignore the facts and tried to convey the impression that nothing had changed.

Union Oil Company's official brochure, which is mailed to stockholders and private citizens around the country, carried a series of color photographs and an article on Santa Barbara in its July/August 1969 issue. The article was titled "Santa Barbara is alive and well in California." No less than twenty-three color photographs depicted children romping in the surf, bikini-clad bathing beauties strolling along the beach, small boats under sail in the harbor, and all the other things that keep Santa Barbarans in Santa Barbara. There was not a single photograph in the entire issue that showed oil on the beach or in the water. There was not a single photo showing the offshore derricks as they appear from the beach. There was, in fact, not a single photograph that would indicate that anything had changed in Santa Barbara. One section of the magazine was devoted to quotes from visiting "outdoors" writers, including those cited above. The section was headlined, "Tell it like it is!" It is unfortunate Union failed to heed its own advice.

During all of this time the voice of opposition was anything but silent. GOO! forces had struck a responsive cord all over the nation, and mail continued to pour in from people who offered moral, political, and financial support.

Residents of Vancouver, British Columbia, traveled all the way to Santa Barbara to see how the citizens there had organized to fight the industry. "Goo Northwest" was formed in Seattle, and "Goo 2" was established in the Los Angeles suburb of Pacific Palisades. Anti-oil forces in New Orleans formed STOP (Stop The Oil Polluters); and KOO (Keep Oil Out) joined the fight in faraway Maine.

It was obvious that the anti-oil sentiment was stronger than a lot of people had expected, and it was also obvious that key public officials were beginning to take notice. Secretary Hickel, whose initial response to Santa Barbara had been far from satisfactory, showed a genuine concern after doing a double-take, but the old Hickel emerged repeatedly as the months slipped past. To his credit, it must be said that Hickel did succeed in establishing tougher regulations governing offshore operations. To his detriment, it must be said that he failed to place conservation ahead of service to the oil industry. For example, he ignored the newly formed Council on Environmental Quality, the President's top advisory agency on antipollution matters, when he announced in October 1970 that leasing of federal parcels in the Gulf of Mexico would be resumed.

Of the thirteen new regulations that Hickel put into effect in 1969, he thought that perhaps the most significant was the one that made oil companies "absolutely liable for pollution." The new regulations also required steel casing to be installed to a greater depth, more frequent testing of blowout prevention devices, more antipollution devices near the platforms, and better warning devices.

Hickel also promised that no further leasing would be offered in the channel without prior public hearings. But while his concern for Santa Barbara did appear genuine, he consistently stopped short of pushing for an all-out victory in the fight to save the channel. In a letter to a member of GOO! dated May 26, 1969, Hickel insisted that he had inherited the problem from his predecessor, Stewart Udall, and that he had to work within the frame of the circumstances as he found them. If the initial decision concerning the awarding of the leases had been his, he said, "quite bluntly, I would have made a different decision from my predecessor."

"Let me stress that the federal leases issued in Santa Barbara Channel prior to my assumption of office constitute binding contracts with the United States and create property rights protected by the Constitution," Hickel wrote. "For this reason, they cannot be arbitrarily cancelled by the Secretary of the Interior. I am certain that, even in the present circumstances, you would not suggest or condone any action on my part which would violate constitutional guarantees or otherwise fail to recognize the limitations on my authority under the governing provisions of law."

Legal minds across the nation generally agreed with Hickel's assessment. They saw no legal way that the leases could be canceled once they had been awarded, unless some kind of agreement could be reached with the lessees. Any attempt to simply cancel the leases would be challenged in the courts by the industry, observers agreed, and the cost to the federal government probably would have totaled well over one billion dollars.

Spokesmen for the oil industry sharply opposed every attempt to cancel any of the leases. To them, the issue was far greater than the Santa Barbara Channel. In the past, the oil industry had enjoyed what virtually amounted to a sacred right to exploit petroleum reserves whenever and wherever they were found. That so-called right was being challenged in Santa Barbara, and the industry pulled out all the stops in an attempt to squelch a rising tide of national sentiment.

Harry Morrison, vice president of the Western Oil and Gas Association, appeared before the Senate's subcommittee on minerals and fuels, and implied that any decision against the oil industry would be a decision against all that is right in America.

"This nation must continue to discover and develop all of its potential petroleum resources," Morrison testified. "And by 'all' we include those resources in the outer continental shelf off California generally, and specifically those in the Santa Barbara Channel area."

The lines of battle were sharply drawn, and the channel thus became an issue of great implications and far-reaching significance. The oil industry saw the movement to save the channel as a direct challenge to its basic *modus operandi*. If the industry lost in Santa Barbara, it could expect to lose elsewhere.

Conservationists also saw the channel as one of the most significant environmental battles in America in decades. They recognized that the deterioration of the environment was approaching the point of no return, and they vowed in vast numbers to make their stand together in Santa Barbara. If they couldn't win there, how could they hope to win anywhere else?

Throughout the long battle, the federal government consistently served the needs of industry more than the needs of the people; sometimes through actions, but more frequently through silence. The role of silence was outlined in a GOO! paper titled "The Santa Barbara Channel Oil Disaster, A Case History of Environmental Exploitation with Recommendations for Reform." The paper stated:

The extent of the "cone of silence" which surrounds the operations of the oil companies can be seen in reports of many conservation agencies which indicate that many scientists associated with universities are reluctant to provide those agencies with information which might be detrimental to the industry, inasmuch as the oil companies are a major source of research funds needed by those scientists, and they are reluctant to jeopardize the continued availability of those funds by making public information detrimental to the industry.

The Interior Department has contributed to the "cone of silence" by attempting to control the free flow of information. For example, employees of the department may be provided with information which is regarded as "proprietary" and then the department may require that employee to sign a statement in which he agrees not to divulge the information, despite the fact that the information may be extremely damaging to the industry or to the department. At times, this requirement may create extreme difficulties for the individual, who may be required by Congress, for example, to divulge information which he is required by the department to withhold. If he refuses to answer the Congressional inquiries, he is in contempt of Congress. If he answers, he is in violation of his agreement with the department. His only recourse is to stand on the Fifth Amendment, which may lead to other, informal sanctions.

In spite of such obstacles, the movement to save Santa Barbara Channel grew, maturing with age and launching this nation into a new era of concern for the environment. Dr. Alan Eschenroeder (Ph.D., engineering, Cornell University), a member of the Santa Barbara City Council, told the story as well as anyone during testimony in March 1970 before the Senate subcommittee on minerals, materials, and fuels.

Many observers felt that after, perhaps, a few months, the entire indignation of Santa Barbara would subside into the *mañana* spirit that is supposed to permeate a serene Southern California City. But it didn't. Inflammation of public fervor spread over the nation. It prompted an Interior Department official to state publicly that Santa Barbara is an open wound in the environment . . . that there is where the action is . . . and that the federal government can't be expected to keep on top of it. Citizen involvement grew, as evidenced by further testimony here. We even had a one-year anniversary commemorative observance of the oil spill arranged by a local citizen's group called the January 28th Committee, which was officially endorsed and sponsored by the City and County of Santa Barbara. It attracted numerous public figures from higher levels of government. Some of the witnesses in this room facing you today sailed out and placed a copy of the Santa Barbara Declaration of Environmental Rights in a buoy floating over the site of the oil well blowout of a year earlier.

Many local causes have their enthusiasm quenched or dissipated much sooner than a year following a crisis. This one not only did not die, but it won national recognition as an eloquent statement of public protest. . . . In courts of law we have fought and, I suppose, have lost rather regularly. But have we lost? We are discussing the issues here today, and that may be something of a relief after the long period of inaction. Supervisor [George] Clyde, who has testified repeatedly on our behalf, and other citizens of the community demanded recognition of our values by you, the federal government, long ago, without any immediate success. Following this and the subsequent damage we suffered, we have entered extensive, and expensive, litigation against some people who might threaten the environment of our corner of the world.

Public hearings have been denied regularly. In fact, one agency of the federal government even changed their rules after they were challenged in court [the Army Corps of Engineers]. This remarkable interpretation of serving the public interest staggers the imagination. Our county and our city asked for hearings months before in numerous official letters approved by elected governing bodies. Only a perfunctory letter response was forthcoming, and another oil-drilling platform was soon to follow. On the local level, we have jointly decided to continue, united, to press these actions to resolution all the way to the highest court, if necessary.

The fight to save the channel was carried out in the citadels of power across the land, in the crowded boardrooms of elected bodies, and in the homes of thousands of citizens who decided quietly to make their stand. But nowhere was the fight more dramatic than on Santa Barbara's municipal pier one year after the blowout at Platform A.

On the first anniversary of the disaster, about five hundred persons gathered on the pier in a sometimes poignant demonstration. The pier served as a loading platform for oil company boats, and the people wanted to set up a temporary blockade in a show of solidarity. Long-haired youths walked beside members of the establishment; blacks joined with whites; the rich sat with the poor; the old talked with the young; they stood together until the sun sank slowly beneath the western horizon, chilling the evening air. As the night wore on, the number dwindled to about a hundred, most of whom huddled together around youths with guitars who strummed songs of lost love, of sorrow, of happiness, of love regained.

Early the next morning, the sun peaked over the coastal hills, setting the channel aflame with new life. People climbed out of sleeping bags, stretched, and readied themselves for a new day. Some seventeen hours after the demonstration had begun, squad cars from the county sheriff's office arrived at the foot of the pier.

Deputies, armed with nightsticks and tear gas, squared themselves off in front of the demonstrators, some of whom they had known for years. It was an awkward, ludicrous moment.

The law is the law, the demonstrators were told, and they could not be allowed to deny the use of the pier to others. They would have to leave, or the deputies would remove them by force. The matter was put to a vote, and the participants decided they had made their point. They would leave.

They stood silently for a moment, and then many joined hands as the demonstration ended with the strains of "America the Beautiful."

5

In the days following the blowout at Platform A, every effort to gain information from sources within the industry and the federal government met with resistance, and ultimately with frustration. Early in the game the federal government admitted that it knew only what the oil industry was willing to tell it, and officials insisted that virtually none of that information could be released to the public. The information was provided to the government, the officials insisted, with the understanding that it not be divulged to competing companies.

As a result, Santa Barbarans watched the oil wash up on their beaches, but they were unable to find out how or why the oil was leaking into the channel. It was thus impossible to determine if the industry was doing everything it could to stop the leak, and if it was at all possible to continue drilling without creating more leaks. When the people tried to find the answer to those questions, they were told by federal representatives simply to "trust us."

It appeared in the beginning that nothing would change that situation, but on February 11, 1969, nearly two weeks after the blowout, President Nixon made an announcement in Washington that caused a new surge of hope. Nixon ordered the formation of a blue-ribbon panel of experts who could examine the problem and tell the people what had happened and how to cope with the disaster. The panel was to include a wide range of distinguished marine geologists, geophysicists, oceanographers, engineers, and wildlife experts.

The task of selecting the members of the panel fell to Dr. Lee A. DuBridge, the President's science adviser and a brilliant scholar of unimpeachable integrity. DuBridge, the former president of California Institute of Technology in Pasadena, had been a Southern California resident for many years, and he knew firsthand of the peculiar problems of Santa Barbara and the Southland. DuBridge picked John C. Calhoun, Jr. as chairman of the panel. Calhoun is vice president for programs and dean of geosciences at Texas A&M University, one of the nation's top training grounds for the petroleum sciences and the alma mater of many of the leaders of the nation's oil business.

DuBridge then named ten other members of the panel: Dr. John Craven, chief scientist, special projects office of the U. S. Navy; Professor Murray F. Hawkins, Jr., head of the department of petroleum engineering at Louisiana State University; Professor Hamilton M. Johnson, chairman of the department of geology at Tulane University; Dr. Gordon MacDonald, vice chancellor for research and graduate affairs at the University of California at Santa Barbara; Dr. Henry W. Menard of San Diego's Scripps Institution of Oceanography; Roy Bobo of Roy Bobo Engineering; Lloyd S. Cluff of Woodward-Clyde and Associates; Ross A. McClintock, president of Fluor Corporation; Dr. Carl H. Savit, vice president of Western Geophysical Company of America, and William R. Lorman of the Naval Civil Engineering Laboratory.

President Nixon told reporters that he had decided to order the formation of the committee following a brief conference with Interior Secretary Hickel. (It was, incidentally, one of the few meetings between the Secretary and the President, and the lack of communications between the two men was one of the things that compelled a frustrated Hickel to make his disenchantment with the President known, and thus one of the things that led ultimately to his excommunication from the power elite in the White House.) Following the conference, Nixon announced that the panel's purpose would be to look into the Santa Barbara oil spill, and then, everybody presumed, to report to the people.

The President's announcement said the ultimate purpose of the panel would be: "To determine the adequacy of existing regulations for all wells licensed in past years now operating off the coast of the United States; to produce far more stringent and effective regulations that will give us better assurance than the nation now has that crises of this kind will not recur.

"This country can no longer afford to squander valuable time before developing answers to pollution and oil slicks from wells, tankers or any other source," the President said. "Every method in existing technology must be developed to control and remove oil pollution. We must also identify those avenues of research where resources will be most profitably committed to solving this problem. These considerations will be among the issues taken up by the group which Dr. DuBridge will assemble."

It was a cautious, innocuous statement.

On February 19, just eight days following the President's announcement, the panel convened in Santa Barbara. There was considerable jubilation over the arrival of the experts, especially from Santa Barbarans who had been rebuffed in their efforts to learn what was causing the leak. Reporters from throughout the state also arrived in Santa Barbara to cover the hearings that the panel was expected to hold.

A press conference, which started an hour late, began with an announcement by Dr. Calhoun, chairman of the panel. The panel, Calhoun said, was meeting in Santa Barbara "to consider problems relating to spilled oil." However, the panel was under specific orders not to conduct "what might be considered an investigation," he said.

Calhoun reported that Dr. DuBridge had mentioned that Hickel was conducting his own review of regulations, and DuBridge's instructions specifically stated: "In order not to prejudice this review, I ask you to avoid consideration of detailed drilling techniques or safety regulations in the Santa Barbara Channel. In no sense should you regard your mission as an investigation of this incident."

Calhoun then exchanged a few comments with some of the reporters. Just as the newsmen were getting down to a little serious questioning, an aide to Hickel moved to Calhoun's side and announced that the press conference was over. The panel, the aide insisted, had to catch an airplane for a flight over the channel. The panel left abruptly and the press conference ended fifteen minutes after it had started.

Just before leaving, Calhoun made one other announcement. The panel planned to meet in Santa Barbara for two days, but all sessions would be closed to the public and to the press.

The panel complied with the instructions fully. There were no "leaks" to the press. There were no other press conferences. All sessions were closed. It was a terribly disturbing turn of events, and it was at that point that some of the more conservative members of the community began to question the way their government was functioning. However, the panel did include a number of top experts, and many people felt it was safe to sit back and await the results of the panel's inquiry.

The bomb dropped on June 2, 1969, more than four months after the blowout.

In a memorandum to the President, Dr. DuBridge reported the findings of the panel. The memo stated:

You will recall that, at the request of Secretary Hickel, you authorized me to establish an expert panel to examine the current oil drill operations in the Santa Barbara Channel and to recommend such actions, particularly on the part of the Union Oil Company and its associated companies, which would:

a) reduce the present oil seepage, and
b) give maximum possibility of avoiding future oil spills.

Our panel consulted at length with petroleum engineers, with members of the U. S. Geological Survey and other experts in the field, and their report is transmitted herewith.

The panel recognized at the outset that there are a variety of different procedures that might be considered, ranging from:

a) immediate suspension of all oil drilling and pumping operations in the vicinity of the Union Oil platform, sealing up, if possible, existing leaks and abandoning the operation to:

b) proceeding to pump the oil as rapidly as possible to remove the oil and reduce its pressure and thus forever prevent future spillage.

There are, of course, a variety of intermediate procedures that might be examined.

The panel has concluded that the maximum safety would be attained by proceeding approximately in accordance with alternative b. Specifically, they recommend that suitable structures be placed over existing leakage areas so the oil now leaking can be contained, and that removal of the oil from the various layers under the Santa Barbara Channel be expedited in order that pressures be reduced which force the oil upward into the ocean, with the eventual idea of removing the oil from the reservoir.

DuBridge added that he agreed with the recommendation because it would "reduce to a minimum current and future hazards of oil leakage."

Specifically, the report made six recommendations:

1) Contain and control oil seepage through the use of underwater receptacles or other suitable methods. (This had already been accomplished, at least in part, by the time the report was issued. Underwater tents were lowered to the channel floor about two months prior to the issuance of the report.)

2) Seal off, or reduce as much as possible, the flow from existing seeps through a program of shallow drilling, pumping, and grouting. (This was actually started immediately

after the blowout when engineers realized that if they could drill into the capping strata and pump mud from several angles they stood a better chance of sealing the leaks.)

3) Review the possible earthquake hazards and take necessary actions. (The report did not name any specific actions.)

4) Attempt, through an oil withdrawal program, to determine the degree of interconnection between levels of the oil-bearing formation. (In other words, find out how easily oil moves from one level, or one reservoir, to another.)

5) Reduce pressures throughout the reservoir to hydrostatic (pressures generated by liquids, including the weight of the water above the bottom of the channel) or less and maintain pressures with water injection, if needed, to minimize subsidence.

6) Deplete all reservoirs within the oil-bearing formation that comprised the Dos Cuadras oil field as efficiently and rapidly as possible consistent with safe practices.

Of the six recommendations, the last two were by far the most controversial. The committee had actually said that the solution to the problem was to drill more, not less. The report ripped through Santa Barbara like an errant bullet.

County Supervisor George Clyde denounced the proposal to increase drilling as a "premature, cheap solution."

At best, Clyde said, such a program would be "a gamble, because if additional blowouts occur, we will have even worse problems than we have right now."

Al Weingand called the report "nonsense, absolute nonsense."

Elsewhere, the report was met with shock. It was hard to believe that a panel of such distinguished scientists and engineers could have come up with such a solution. The people of Santa Barbara angrily demanded to know how and why the panel had reached that conclusion. What kind of scientific evidence did they have to back up their recommendations?

Scores of people, including some elected officials and many

representatives of the press, asked the federal government
for a fuller explanation. Each request was met with an
emphatic "no." The geological information about the channel,
and specifically about Union Oil Company's operations on
Tract 402, had been made available to the government in
absolute confidence, and high government officials insisted
that the confidence would not be violated.

It was a stunning maneuver, and thousands of people who
had been willing to sit on the sidelines and let the government proceed in its own way decided to join the fight. The
fence straddlers had suddenly found themselves without a
fence.

Santa Barbara City Councilman Alan Eschenroeder flew
to Washington in an effort to gain more information. He
returned to his city empty-handed.

California's Democratic Senator Alan Cranston called repeatedly for the release of the information, both in cor-
respondence to high Administration officials and in public
meetings and rallys across the state. In a letter to the Los
Angeles *Times,* Cranston pointed out that the report "was
based on investigations and testimony which have not been
released to the public and which we are asked to take at
face value. Most of the testimony came from the Union
Oil Co. and U. S. Geological Survey; the two parties responsible for the disaster in the first place."

To all requests the answer was the same, from the President
of the United States down. No information would be made
public; the people would have to trust the officials and the
industry that had made such drastic mistakes in the past.

In October 1969, the panel issued a second report, considerably better than the first, but still lacking in essential
information. The second report called for immediate federal
funding of research, development, and operation of a program to control massive oil spills. The report also had something to say about the general subject of offshore drilling:

"At present, disputes about the development of new offshore mineral resource areas are usually between exploitation

now and prohibition of development for all time. We suggest that there are potential offshore resources which fall into neither of these categories and that wise employment of our natural resources and preservation of our environment are ill served by the existence of those two extreme positions."

The report recommended that some resources be placed in "escrow" for fixed periods of time to control their orderly development, but it made no specific mention of Santa Barbara in that regard.

Perhaps most significant of all, the report recommended strongly that local areas be given a greater voice in the exploitation of natural resources, specifically in public hearings prior to the commencement of development.

"The holding of hearings is a costly and time-consuming process and if there were any other way of accomplishing the same goal we would happily recommend it, but we feel there is no satisfactory substitute for hearing a variety of views in a public forum. In the case of resources that have been exploited there is no second chance. Under these circumstances all interested groups should be heard and their opinions brought to the attention of those responsible for making decisions."

In that same general area, the report stated:

"Common sense and the public interest demand that adequate information be available to those making decisions about offshore resources. We therefore recommend that, through negotiation, purchase or possibly regulation, data necessary for resource evaluation held by private companies, state and local governments and any other parties to exploration and development of offshore mineral resources be made available to those who must make decisions about their exploitation."

Shortly after the panel issued its second report, the Department of the Interior released Geological Survey Professional Paper 679. That paper, which was discussed fully in Chapter 3, gave a comprehensive review of the Santa Barbara area, and it answered many of the questions that had been haunting critics of the DuBridge panel.

In testimony a short time later before the Senate's subcommittee on minerals, materials, and fuels, Dr. Eschenroeder expressed gratitude for the release of the paper, and then he added:

"Unfortunately, we always seem to get the data well after the decisions are made and implemented."

The paper was released one full year after the blowout at Platform A.

There are two factors that are particularly troubling about the DuBridge reports. One is the composition of the panel itself, and the other is the scope of the investigation and the extent of the reports.

Robert L. Jackson, a Los Angeles *Times* reporter who specializes in covering federal regulatory agencies in Washington, D.C., conducted an investigation into the background on the members of the panel. He found that at least five of the eleven members had been dependent upon Union Oil Company or its partners in the channel lease for partial support of their businesses or professions. On January 18, 1970, Jackson reported his findings in the *Times:*

Ross A. McClintock, president of Fluor Corporation, of Los Angeles—Fluor Corporation had contracts with Union Oil both before and after McClintock's service on the panel.

Carl H. Savit, vice president of Western Geophysical Company of America, Houston—Savit's firm did hundreds of thousands of dollars worth of business with Union Oil in long-range programs. In addition, the firm has held contracts in various parts of the world with all three of Union's lease partners, Texaco, Gulf, and Mobil.

John C. Calhoun, Jr., a vice president of Texas A&M University; Hamilton M. Johnson, chairman of the department of geology, Tulane University; and Murray F. Hawkins, Jr., head of the department of petroleum engineering, Louisiana State University—all three schools shared in grants from Union, Texaco, Gulf, and Mobil totaling $179,000 over a five-year period.

Jackson confronted Dr. DuBridge, as well as all five members of the panel, with his findings and all responded that they saw no conflict of interest, although they conceded the financial ties.

"They [the members of the panel] had to have a thorough knowledge of geology and petroleum engineering," DuBridge told Jackson. "No uninformed person or nonexpert could be involved on this panel. There are no clear-cut or obvious conflicts of interest, although all the members necessarily had connections with the oil business. I am utterly confident in their total integrity."

Calhoun, chairman of the panel, told Jackson he was insulted by any suggestion that his objectivity might have been compromised.

"The president of Gulf Oil is a graduate of Texas A&M," Calhoun said. "Key leaders throughout the industry are graduates of ours and other universities represented on the panel. You can find many ties between the industry and our universities."

Although Jackson found no evidence of ties between the other six members of the panel and Union Oil Company or its partners, all were executives with corporations or agencies that could only have benefited from findings that would have aided the oil industry or the general field of ocean science, including offshore drilling. In this regard, it is worth noting that the blowout at Platform A occurred at a critical time for anyone engaged in oceanography.

There had been much speculation in the late 1960s to the effect that this nation was entering its golden age of ocean exploration. Numerous corporations, as well as educational institutions, made substantial investments on oceanography and undersea equipment. The ocean was seen as a great storehouse of mineral wealth, as well as a farmland where crops could be harvested to provide nourishment for the exploding population of a shrinking world. Man could use the ocean to solve some of his most pressing problems, and it seemed, a decade ago, that this country was heading in that direction.

But somewhere along the way the cities began to come apart at the seams, crime waves threatened to destroy the nation's delicate legal fabric, and Americans became painfully aware of the fact that millions were living in poverty right here in the land of plenty. The country had also set its sights on exploring outer space, a far more dramatic program than oceanography, and what money was available for exploration went mainly into the space program.

Numerous corporations, including such giants as Lockheed and Westinghouse, had invested millions in the development of undersea equipment, such as deep-sea submersibles. The equipment was developed with the idea that an aggressive national program of ocean exploration was just around the corner, and an industrial program of deep-sea exploitation—including offshore oil operations—would not be far behind. But as the 1960s drew to a close, the national program was anything but aggressive. Submersibles worth millions of dollars went up on blocks, and corporations pondered the problem of retrieving their investment.

In short, the bottom was already dropping out of oceanography when oil began bubbling to the surface aound Platform A.

The timing of the blowout was critical. More than any other event in U.S. history, the blowout caused more people to ask for a cautious policy on man's intrusion into the sea. The blowout thus emerged as a painful experience for an ailing discipline; and nearly anyone engaged in any aspect of the ocean sciences was particularly sensitive to the blowout and all subsequent effects. They realized that negative findings by the DuBridge panel could set the offshore exploration program back at least a decade.

Given those conditions, and assuming the integrity of the members of the panel, the result of the panel's investigation was virtually predetermined. It would have been unrealistic to have expected anything but a very limited report, answering only the most pressing questions, and deliberately avoiding areas that could have had a serious impact upon the oil industry's offshore program. For the most part, the reports dealt with only one problem: how to stop the leak beneath Platform A.

In that regard, most experts believe the findings of the panel were accurate.

No one can be absolutely certain what caused the leak, but the general consensus is that expanding gases in deep reservoirs forced oil and gas up through flaws in the capping layer and into shallow reservoirs, and finally out through fractures in the channel's floor. Most experts believe the oil and gas traveled up the shaft of well A-21 for a considerable distance before it was bled off to the side within a few hundred feet of the bottom of the channel.

In this regard, one point is particularly important. There are procedures for insuring against such an occurrence, the most important of which is the laying of casing within the well during the drilling stage. Suppose a workman bored a hole into the ground and then withdrew the bit. If he had punctured a tank below the surface that contained liquid under extreme pressure, the liquid would flow up the shaft and onto the ground. Suppose, however, he had stopped drilling every now and then and forced sections of pipe into the hole, connecting each pipe to the section just ahead. If he had connected a nozzle to the end of the pipe at the top of the hole, he could control the flow by closing the nozzle.

That may be an oversimplification, but it generally is what drillers do when drilling for oil. Every now and then they remove the drill and lay a little more casing until the casing extends a thousand feet or so into the ground. That way, if oil begins flowing up the shaft, it will be forced to travel inside the casing, which is equipped with shutoff valves.

In Union Oil's well A-21, however, the casing was not laid to a depth of one thousand feet. At the time of the blowout, the well had been drilled to a total depth of 3479 feet. Only 238 feet of casing had been set in the shaft. Critics of Union charged after the blowout that more casing should have been set long before the well reached such a great depth. Workmen on the platform had planned to do that later, but they never got the chance.

The oil probably traveled up the shaft until it reached a weakness in the capping layer—possibly three hundred or four hundred feet below the bottom of the channel—and then branched off through fractures in the rocks. No one can be certain, but even Union's president Fred Hartley said in congressional testimony that if the casing had been laid to a greater depth the well would not have blown out.

The DuBridge panel concluded that the oil from the deeper reservoirs eventually reached shallow reservoirs, literally raising the pressure to the bursting point. It followed, then, that if the pressure could be reduced, the flow of oil into the channel could be stopped. The only logical conclusion, the panel decided, was to continue pumping until the pressure returned to normal.

Well enough.

But what about the rest of the channel? Did the committee feel it was safe to continue developing other leases throughout the channel? Was it possible to remove the oil without massive contamination? In view of the unstable nature of the channel, should the federal government have called it quits while there was still time, prohibiting further drilling and reimbursing the oil companies? In short, was it safe to continue?

It stands as an open indictment of the DuBridge panel that those questions were not answered.

The real tragedy of the DuBridge panel is not in what it said, but in what it failed to say. While pointing to the desperate need for new equipment to deal with major oil spills, the panel neglected to say the obvious—that this nation is nowhere near ready to engage in offshore operations in an area as unpredictable and unstable as the Santa Barbara Channel.

That failure was at least partly the result of the composition of the panel. The panel produced just the kind of report that should have been expected—a report that cleared the way for further exploitation. One wonders how the report would have been effected if the panel had also had a few environmentalists and marine biologists. Would they have ignored the need for answers to other questions?

The panel's reports puzzled many and infuriated others. Senator Cranston suggested that the panel had been stacked with industry sympathizers, and he called—unsuccessfully— for a new study by a "totally independent" group.

"A body like the National Academy of Science could certainly receive testimony from oil companies and people who work for the industry," Cranston told the *Times'* Jackson. "But it would evaluate this testimony from an independent stand. The present panel relied largely on oil company data without gathering independent data of its own."

The people of Santa Barbara had expected a comprehensive report from the DuBridge panel, but they did not get it. The tragedy is that if the panel had produced the kind of report that the evidence clearly called for, the people would have had a valuable tool to aid in the fight to save their environment. But the report served only the needs of the industry and virtually ignored the most significant facts available. And in time it was back to business as usual in the Santa Barbara Channel. In testimony before the U. S. Senate subcommittee on minerals, materials, and fuels, Senator Cranston said in part:

There is one new element that was added to the Santa Barbara Channel several months ago on which I would like to comment briefly. Humble [Oil and Refining Company] has made a large new oil discovery some fifteen miles west of the Santa Barbara sanctuary and about five miles offshore. Dr. Thomas Barrow, senior vice president of Humble, testifying yesterday before this committee, said that in order to produce oil on this lease it will be necessary to have some platforms above water, although there could possibly be some satellite platforms completed underwater.

An above-water platform on the Humble lease would be a structure of incredible proportions. According to the U. S. Geological Survey, the water on the Humble lease is 1100 feet deep. If the platform and drilling rig rose 165 feet above the ocean surface, as does Union's Platform A, then we are talking about a structure 1265 feet high. By contrast, the Empire State Building is 1250 feet high—just fifteen feet shorter. The deepest drilling platform put into operation as of this date is in 380 feet of water.

In other words, to develop its lease Humble will have to erect a structure taller than the world's second-tallest building, and it will have to drill in water at almost three times the depth of any well presently producing oil from a drilling platform. What happens if there is a blowout, an aggravated seep, or a leak at 1100 feet? We cannot use divers at that depth. Even tethered divers from a diving bell have never even attempted to operate at these depths. The world record for such a dive is 1000 feet.

The normal maximum operating depth for divers is 400 feet. At the depths such as those involved on the Humble lease, we would have to depend entirely on mechanical devices attached to underwater submarines. None of the techniques involved in producing oil at such depths have been put into practice before. No submarine has ever tried to repair a malfunction of a drilling platform at 1100 feet. No underwater device ever tried to capture oil leaking from a fissure in the ocean floor at anywhere near this depth.

In short, we do not have any reason to believe that we can drill safely on the Humble lease. To allow Humble to go ahead as they are planning to do, is to take grave and unwarranted risks with the environmental health and safety of the Santa Barbara Channel. At this time, when techniques for oil drilling in deeper waters are still theoretical, the risks are far too great for the federal government to inflict them on the coast of California. These resources clearly should be held in reserve until that time in the future when we know how to produce oil safely, particularly at such depths, and until we have completed techniques for underwater completions of drilling rigs [thus eliminating the unsightly platforms].

Why couldn't the DuBridge panel have said that?

6

It appeared in the beginning that legislative action to correct the sins against Santa Barbara would be swift and to the point. Less than a month after the blowout, Senator Alan Cranston announced plans to introduce legislation to "ban all drilling" in the channel. Cranston revealed the plan before about eight hundred persons during a rally on the waterfront overlooking the channel and the oil platforms. But his bill was only one of many. Within six weeks after the blowout, no less than forty-four bills dealing with offshore oil pollution were pending in the U. S. Congress. Still others were introduced in the California state legislature.

Most of the bills were aimed at making the oil companies more responsible for damage; some sought to limit drilling through such things as setting up sanctuaries; and others attempted to give local agencies more control over offshore operations.

Not one piece of major legislation concerning offshore oil operations passed either the U. S. Congress or the state legislature. Indeed, not even one major piece of offshore legislation even reached the floor of either house of the U. S. Congress. That record was grossly disappointing to many residents of Santa Barbara who had always thought they understood how the legislative system worked. Like most Americans, they were under the impression that when a bill is introduced, it is well on its way to becoming law or at least to being discussed. Not so.

The fact of the matter is that only a small percentage of bills introduced each session are seriously considered by either house of the U. S. Congress. There are many reasons. Most bills simply are not worth the effort. Sometimes, they are introduced by a legislator—who knows they will not pass—just to get some of his constituents off his back. One California lawmaker got so mad one evening while he was waiting for a table in a restaurant that a short time later he introduced a bill that would have required all restaurants in the state to seat their patrons within fifteen minutes of their reservation time. The bill never passed because no one thought it was worth considering. It was, unfortunately, about as valuable as thousands of other bills offered each year.

Nearly twenty thousand bills have been introduced during recent sessions (two-year periods) of the U. S. Congress. It would be physically impossible to give serious consideration to so many bills, many of which were worthless in the first place. As a result, only about 10 percent even stood a remote chance of passing.

When the founders of America were writing the U. S. Constitution, they decided to let the Senate and the House decided how to handle their own internal procedural matters. Anticipating the flood of bills, the two bodies established a system through which bills could be examined, evaluated, and considered. Under the system, the two houses were divided into committees that could pay closer attention to bills that fell within each committee's general area of responsibility. Over the years, state legislatures evolved similarly until the country reached its present predicament: nation governed by committees.

The system accomplished its fundamental purpose: It permitted a closer examination of various bills by a few lawmakers, who could then recommend passage or rejection to the rest of the legislators.

Unfortunately, the system also has certain weaknesses. It has established a hierarchy within each house, creating overlords who wield tremendous power. Members of the Senate and the House who become chairmen of certain committees are in a position to breathe life or death into almost any bill that comes their way. By simply refusing to place the bill before his committee, or by convincing members of the committee to reject it, the chairman is in a key position to influence major legislation—and to help his friends. It is little wonder that these men are fawned over and catered to by junior members of Congress.

The system once provoked Woodrow Wilson to describe American government as "government by the standing committees of Congress." The committees, he remarked, could send a bill into "dim dungeons of silence whence it will never return."

It is little wonder, then, that powerful special-interest groups watch with great concern when the chairmanship of a key committee shifts into new hands. And it is by no accident that Russell Long, for example, is the chairman of the Senate Finance Committee, and thus one of the most powerful men in the entire federal government. Nearly any bill that would affect the profits of the oil industry must pass through Long's committee, and he has stated publicly that he considers it part of his job to protect the interests of the oil business.

In this regard, it is important to note that the most powerful men in Washington and in state capitals across the land are not just the elected representatives. They are the richly financed lobbyists who have the means to offer financial assistance to political campaigns, and who manipulate scores of lawmakers in the federal Congress and in every state legislature in the nation. They control the money, which controls the campaigns, which influence the voters. Their will, when it comes to the selection of committee members and chairmen, cannot be ignored.

The committees, and their many subcommittees, are so numerous that their actions are rarely covered by news media, except when they are conducting important hearings. The odds are that when the bill is put to a vote, no reporter will be present. The legislator knows it is highly unlikely that any great number of his constituents will ever know how he voted. Only his lobbyist will know for sure.

There are other ways of getting around considering legislation that would be uncomfortable for the lawmakers. When a bill is first introduced, it is given a number and then referred to a committee. Some bills are automatically given the kiss of death simply by being referred to a committee that is predisposed one way or the other. Bills may be referred to a committee that has so many other pressing matters that it is impossible to consider another, or even in some cases to a committee that is not particularly concerned about the subject of the bill. In the U. S. Congress, bills are referred to committees by the Speaker in the House, and by the presiding officer in the Senate.

Even if a bill emerges successfully from committee, it is still a long way from passage. This is especially true in the House, where each bill reported out of committee must pass through the powerful House Rules Committee before it can be voted upon by the legislators. More bills are reported out of committee each session than can possibly be considered by the House. It is the responsibility of the Rules Committee to establish priorities, theoretically selecting those that are most pressing to present first.

But it is also a convenient way to dispose of a bill that most of the lawmakers would prefer not to have to vote on, thus reducing the chance of having an unpopular vote come back to haunt them during a campaign. This is done simply by placing the bill at the bottom of the stack, thereby reducing the chance that it will reach the floor of the House.

The situation is even worse in many state legislatures. In California, for example, bills in the state Senate are referred to committee by the Senate Rules Committee. For years, the committee has killed unwanted legislation simply by referring it to the wrong committees.

What this all adds up to is that it is not necessary for powerful groups to control all members of a legislative body in order to have their way. They do not even have to control

most members. All they have to do is control the right
ones, and through them they can call the shots the way
they want them.

Alas, anyone who has worked with conservationists or
consumer organizations has heard the plaintive cry over and
over: "If we could just get our bill onto the floor, no one
would dare vote against it . . ."

It was no accident that not even one of the major bills
concerning offshore operations reached the floor of either
house of the U. S. Congress. The system worked just as it
was supposed to work—for the protection of those powerful
figures who move quietly behind the scenes to pull the strings
that seal the fate of each of the bills.

Although none of the bills reached the floor, several
hearings were held by committees. Three of the bills are
particularly worth noting: separate bills authored by Cranston
and Senator Edmund Muskie to end all drilling in the
channel; and former Senator George Murphy's bill to create
a federal sanctuary in the channel, wiping out twenty of
the seventy-one leases. (Murphy, a Republican, was defeated
in the 1970 general election by Democrat John Tunney.)

Of the three, only Murphy's stood a chance of passing.
The Nixon Administration had let it be known that it would
not support the other bills, since it did not favor backing
out of all of the channel leases. There was little chance
that either Cranston's or Muskie's bill would gather enough
support to pass without the Administration's backing, and,
even if they passed, there was the threat of a presidential
veto.

Murphy's bill was co-sponsored in the House by Con-
gressman Charles Teague, a Santa Barbara Republican. The
bill was the result of numerous behind-the-scene negotiations between representatives of the Administration, the oil
industry, and members of Congress.

The bill called for extending the existing state sanctuary
along the coast of Santa Barbara all the way to Santa Cruz
Island, about twenty miles offshore, thus killing twenty of

the seventy-one leases in the channel. No drilling would be permitted within the sanctuary, and the oil companies that had purchased the leases would be reimbursed with funds from increased production on a naval oil reserve at Elk Hills, California. The amount of reimbursement would be determined by the courts.

Union Oil Company's Tract 402—where Platform A was located—was within the area of the proposed sanctuary, but according to the bill it would be excluded in order to permit continued efforts to reduce the pressure in the reservoir. By the time the bill was introduced, incidentally, the tract was producing enough oil to make a substantial profit for its owners.

Another tract, just south of 402, had already been abandoned by Humble Oil and Refining Company—because it was dry. As it turned out, no one knew for sure if there were any significant deposits within the entire proposed sanctuary, except for the one tract that was excluded from the plan—Union's 402. Rich deposits had been found on each side of the sanctuary, but every hole drilled within the area itself turned out dry.

The oil industry insisted that it wanted to hang onto the leases on the chance that there could be oil in the sanctuary, but the people of Santa Barbara were sure they had smelled a rat.

George H. Clyde, chairman of the county Board of Supervisors, strongly denounced the bill before the U. S. Senate Interior and Insular Affairs Committee in July 1970:

Enactment of this bill would do virtually nothing—in fact, it would do worse than nothing. It would give the sham appearance of solving the "Santa Barbara problem," yet it would solve not a thing. Such action would be tokenism in its worst form and make an honest solution all the more difficult to achieve.

All evidence leads to the conclusion that there is little oil in these twenty leases. By canceling these leases only, you would be doing little or nothing to prevent future oil spill disasters. By not canceling the remaining fifty-one oil leases on either side of this corridor—some of which having already been proved to be rich in oil—you will be inviting more disastrous spills that will result in pollution of the waters and beaches in Southern California.

The only positive aspect of S.4017 [Murphy's bill] is that the Administration has at long last accepted the fact that leases can and should be canceled when they were erroneously let in the first place. This is a major step forward, and Santa Barbara County would gladly support S.4017, if it were amended to include all the leases in the Channel.

Clyde, who was active in Santa Barbara's fight in the very beginning, went on to discuss several lesser bills and finally ended his testimony with these observations:

I should like to make the following comments and, for one moment, digress slightly. As you all know, we have had three serious riots within the last six months at the University of California's campus in Santa Barbara County. These have resulted in one death, numerous injuries, property damage, and hundreds of arrests. I have had numerous contacts with the students—particularly with the moderate students who are not bank burners and who would like to work within the system. One of their major complaints and frustrations is the inability of our society to correct quickly and completely its ills. This is a frustration that is nationwide, not only among students, but among large segments of our society. It is a frustration which in Santa Barbara finds a perfect example in the Channel oil problem. We all know that there are many of society's ills which cannot be corrected quickly and completely—but in the Santa Barbara Channel we do have a blatant ill which can be corrected quickly and almost completely by the simple act of Congress doing what is right.

We are in this situation. The Administration has finally come to the conclusion that a grievous error, committed in a previous Administration, can be corrected by canceling the actions of that previous Administration. The only problem is that this Administration has not seen fit to do the major surgery necessary—in fact, it has only proposed a minor face-lifting, which will sag horribly when the inevitable spills and pollution occur. It is up to Congress to do the major surgery, to do what is right and to enact legislation terminating all the leases in the Santa Barbara Channel.

A lack of aggressive support from the people of Santa Barbara no doubt hurt the bill's chances of passing, but there was little chance that it would have made it anyway. The bill died in committee in 1970, and it was reintroduced in 1971. One of the problems in winning passage for a bill that is related primarily to a limited geographical area is that most members of Congress have little or no reason to support the measure. It is simply a matter of the age-old question, "What's in it for me?"

In politics, that is a legitimate question. The sale of the leases in the channel netted the federal government 602 million dollars in bonuses alone. Royalties over the years from oil production were expected to surpass that figure many times. It would have been tremendously expensive for the federal government to back out of the program, and everybody knew it. The cost of reimbursement to the industry for the canceled leases alone would have totaled at least one billion dollars, according to most educated guesses. Why should a senator from an interior state—say Utah, for example—vote to take money out of his constituents' pockets to help far-off Santa Barbara?

When Murphy's bill was introduced in the Senate, it was referred to the Committee on Interior and Insular Affairs, which in turn referred it to its Subcommittee on Minerals, Materials, and Fuels. The chairman of the subcommittee was Senator Frank E. Moss of Utah, a Democrat. Of the full committee's seventeen members, thirteen were from interior states. To them, the question of "What's in it for me?" was real indeed.

The subcommittee began serious consideration of Murphy's bill on Tuesday, July 21, 1970. In his opening remarks, Chairman Moss said the subcommittee had turned to Murphy's bill because it was the only Santa Barbara bill backed by the Administration. Moss went on to say:

From comments heard in Santa Barbara and elsewhere, I gather that there is some fairly strong feeling that we have had enough hearings, enough consideration, and that we now should act forthwith. I understand and, to a point, am sympathetic with that feeling. But there are several factors that must be considered.

First and foremost is the over-all precedent involved. If the citizens of Santa Barbara have a right to have the federal government take property belonging to citizens—and an oil lease is a property right—then the citizens of every other coastal area everywhere along the coasts of the United States have that same right.

Under our American system of government, just compensation, in the words of the Constitution, for the taking of property is mandatory. Cancellation of leases, or the shutting down of operations on them, would cost the taxpayers tremendous sums—many hundreds of millions of dollars, perhaps even billions. Surely, in this time of critical national priorities for money for our cities, for education, for health, and most of all for defense, we must do some "balancing of the equities."

Then there is the perhaps more far-reaching effect on our national security if production of oil from the continental shelf were to be terminated, in fact. A great policy controversy now is raging in the government and elsewhere over oil import controls. Our nation must be substantially self-sufficient in this essential energy resource, and that means we must not, we cannot, be dependent upon foreign oceanborne sources, many of which have been proved to be unstable.

The recent report of the Public Land Law Review Commission states that proved reserves in the federal area of the shelf are 2.9 billion barrels of oil and 30.3 billion cubic feet of gas. Those figures are for proved reserves only. Estimated reserves are 34 to 220 billion barrels of petroleum liquids and 170 to 1100 trillion cubic feet of natural gas.

Furthermore, we do need the oil. Just recently, President Nixon's science adviser, Dr. Lee A. DuBridge, warned that "we may have to mount a national campaign to reduce the use of air conditioners and other electrical equipment" because of the threat of substantial power shortages in many parts of the country. The President's adviser warned of blackouts and shutting down of industrial plants.

We should not take hastily any action that would foreclose development of this great, this essential, natural resource. And what's good for Santa Barbara must be good for the rest of America. That is, every other area under the American flag has equal rights with respect to preventing production of a resource essential to our national security.

Now, in conclusion . . . it is necessary for us to realize that there is more, much more, involved than a single area or a single state.

As far as I myself am concerned, I am proud of my record as a conservationist and protector of environmental quality. I have labored long and hard for such legislation and its fulfillment, and at times have had the honor of being a leader in such development.

However, because what we do will have such far-reaching import, let us act in accordance with the old classical maxim, let us "make haste slowly."

There is evidence that Moss's remarks grew out of a genuine concern to do what is right rather than an attempt to serve the interests of the oil industry. Ronnie Dugger, writing in *The Atlantic* (September 1969), tells a story that was related to him by former Illinois Senator Paul Douglas. During the 1957–58 political campaign, the oil industry was greatly concerned over who the new faces might be in the new Congress, when the old question of the oil depletion allowance was expected to come up for a showdown, again. According to Dugger, an official with the national Democratic senatorial campaign committee was sent west to offer financial help to several senatorial candidates on the condition that they vote to uphold the tax loophole.

One of the candidates the emissary approached was Moss, a county attorney who was running for his first term in the Senate. Moss was offered ten thousand dollars for his campaign if he would agree to help uphold the depletion allowance. That would have amounted to a monumental campaign contribution on Utah standards.

Moss reportedly thought about the matter for a moment, and then replied that he simply was not sure if the depletion allowance was a good thing or not. He said he could not say how he would vote until he had a chance to study it a little more, so he would just have to turn down the offer.

The emissary was astonished. He had found an honest candidate, and under the rules of the game he could not help him win the election. It reportedly troubled the official so much that he returned to Washington, telephoned a wealthy liberal Democrat in New York, and the Democrat sent Moss a ten-thousand-dollar campaign contribution with no strings attached. Moss won the election.

Like Moss, many senators and congressmen from interior states were deeply concerned about the Santa Barbara problem, but they were afraid that any move to save the channel through legislation could paralyze the nation's energy sources, since similar concessions would have to be made elsewhere if they were made in Santa Barbara. Many were also concerned over their own constituents, believing their voters would take a dim view of their elected representatives spending so much money to help far-off Santa Barbara.

But many of the voters were more sophisticated than their representatives had anticipated. The truth of the matter is that Santa Barbara was never just a local issue. Of the thousands upon thousands of letters received at the GOO! office—many containing money to help in the fight—approximately half came from residents of interior states. They recognized that the channel had become more than a local environmental issue; it had become the *cause célèbre*. It represented all that was foul in the environment—greed and insensitivity on the part of industry, failure on the part of government, frustration on the part of the citizens.

There are other considerations that should have troubled the senators. While Santa Barbara may have seemed a long way from Utah, the ocean belongs to all people, and there may come a day when the people of Utah will depend upon the ocean for much of their food. It is amazing that such a fact should have escaped the senators as they sat down for dinner night after night—lobster from Maine, king crab from Alaska, tuna and a little soul food from Southern California. Faraway Santa Barbara? It is only as far away as the dinner table.

While the legislative fight was under way, the effort to save the channel was being pursued on several other fronts as well. Two days after Secretary Hickel permitted resumption of drilling in the channel, Santa Barbara County Counsel George P. Kading filed suit in federal court seeking an injunction to halt the resumption of drilling. The American Civil Liberties Union joined in the legal fight, contending that the oil spill had caused irreparable damage to beaches and parks.

Over the months the legal fight took various turns. A federal court in Los Angeles refused to block operations in the channel, so the people appealed to a higher court. On November 12, 1969, nearly ten months after the blowout, the U. S. Ninth Circuit Court of Appeals in San Francisco issued a temporary restraining order halting the granting of government permits for drilling new oil wells and erecting drilling platforms off the Santa Barbara coast. The order was issued at the request of the city and county, and eighteen conservationists represented by the ACLU. The temporary order was not followed by a permanent injunction, and the ban was lifted a few days later. The industry was thus permitted to continue its operations while the question of the permanent injunction was being considered by the court— a procedure that could have taken months, if not years. The people immediately took their case to the U. S. Supreme Court. They asked the high court to remove the case from the circuit court and decide the issue itself. At stake was the basic concept that Americans have a constitutional right to a clean environment.

The people also asked the Supreme Court to stop the industry from erecting more platforms while the issue was being decided. The petition argued that by the time the appellate court had resolved the issue, the channel would "begin to take on the appearance of a forest of oil derricks."

The petition insisted that the public has a right to full-scale hearings prior to any drilling. But on November 25, 1969, the high court refused to issue a restraining order and sent the issue back to the San Francisco circuit court. Nearly three months later, the circuit court refused to ban the drillings, thus rejecting the argument that federal laws under which the drilling was permitted were unconstitutional because they did not require public hearings.

In the meantime, on January 13, 1970, a 343-count criminal complaint was filed against Union, Mobil, Texaco, and Gulf by Santa Barbara District Attorney David Minier. The eighty-seven-page complaint charged that the companies polluted state waters in the channel.

California state and local agencies filed a series of suits the following month against the federal government of five hundred million dollars in damages. Another damage suit was filed in behalf of shoreline private property owners from Santa Barbara to San Diego, asking for damages expected to total at least three hundred million dollars.

The suits, filed in federal court in Los Angeles, charged that the federal drilling supervisor, Donald W. Solanas, negligently caused the blowout by "failing to perform his duty." Solanas had admitted that neither he nor anyone from his office had been on Platform A during the entire time that A-21 was being drilled.

One of the suits, brought on behalf of all public entities and agencies, claimed:

Plantiffs' lands cannot be used for their usual purposes.

Plaintiff State of California's tide and submerged lands no longer will support plant life necessary for the survival and propagation of fish.

Plaintiffs' personal property has been damaged and in some cases has been rendered unusable.

And, additionally, plaintiffs have expended large amounts of money to prevent or ameliorate further damage, to clean up the current damage and to restore to its previous state the real property and chattels described.

By the time the second anniversary of the blowout at Platform A rolled around, however, no major battles had been won in the courts by the people of Santa Barbara. One reason the people lost on so many fronts lies in the fact that the federal regulations governing the drilling failed to pin the liability for oil spills where it belonged—on the oil companies themselves.

Secretary Hickel sought to change that soon after the blowout. On February 17, 1969, Hickel signed an amendment to the federal regulations that placed future liability squarely on the shoulders of the oil companies. The amendment stated:

The lessee shall not pollute the waters of the high seas or damage the aquatic life of the sea or allow extraneous matter to enter and damage any mineral- or water-bearing formation. The lessee shall dispose of all useless liquid products of wells in a manner acceptable to the supervisor.

If the waters of the sea are polluted by the drilling or

production operations of the lessee, and such pollution damages or threatens to damage aquatic life, wildlife, or public or private property, the control and removal of the pollutant and the reparation of any damage, to whomsoever occurring, proximately resulting therefrom shall be at the expense of the lessee, and on failure of the lessee to control and remove the pollutant the supervisor, in cooperation with other appropriate agencies of the federal, state and local governments, or in cooperation with the lessee, or both, shall have the right to accomplish the control and removal of the pollutant at the cost of the lessee, but such action shall not relieve the lessee of responsibility for reparation of damages as provided herein.

The amendment told oil companies in effect that even if it was not their fault, if they messed it up, they were going to clean it up and repair any damages. Three months later, Hickel expanded the regulations by imposing unlimited liability on polluters.

Other regulations were also put into effect in an attempt to reduce the threat of pollution, but in the words of Supervisor Clyde, they were "woefully inadequate and meaningless froth."

According to the Los Angeles *Times,* one international drilling company examined the "tough new regulations," and in an effort to comply laid out a total cash expenditure of $861. The only new item needed was a back-up safety valve.

Of all the new regulations signed by Hickel, the "unlimited liability" was by far the most significant. It spoke the language of the oil industry—money.

In Los Angeles, at the headquarters of Union Oil Company, a company lawyer hastily sent word up the chain of command, telling executives that the new regulation would not be retroactive, thereby reducing the chance that Union would be clobbered in the courts.

The new regulation quickly made the rounds of executive

boardrooms in the headquarters of oil companies across the
nation, and among the insurance companies that in the
past had paid the bills when the companies goofed. Aetna
Life & Casualty Company of Hartford, Conn., which paid
Union five million dollars to cover the cost of cleaning
up the beaches in Santa Barbara, sent a memo to all field
offices stating that it no longer would insure oil companies
against spills. Other companies followed suit.

The oil industry, of course, set up an immediate howl
of protest, claiming that the new liability was unfair, unjust,
and a blow below the belt. But the ruling survived intact.

It was, however, nearly a year before the industry felt
the first bite from the government's new stance. On February 10, 1970, fire erupted on Chevron Oil Company's
automatic Platform Charlie in the Gulf of Mexico, thirty
miles southeast of New Orleans. The platform, standing on
stilts in forty feet of water, controlled twelve wells.

Nearly a month later the fire finally was snuffed out with a
four-hundred-pound charge of dynamite, but oil from eight
wells spurted a hundred feet into the air, staining the Gulf
of Mexico with the biggest oil spill in history. Workmen
pumped drilling mud into the wells, but it was not until
March 31—seven weeks after the fire had begun—that the
final well was capped. When it was all over, it became
apparent that the Gulf Coast had escaped an ecological disaster of staggering proportions only through the benevolence
of nature.

More than twenty thousand barrels of oil leaked into the
Gulf during the spill—possibly twice as much as spilled
into the Santa Barbara Channel following the blowout at
Platform A. A Bird refuge on Breton Island near New Orleans was fouled by the giant slick, but conservationists set
off firecrackers to frighten birds away, and the damage was
not as bad as had been feared. There was otherwise little
effect from the spill because nature decided to be kind in
the spring of 1970 to men who had earned only her wrath.
Normally, the predominant winds out of the south would

have driven the huge slick into the estuaries of the Mississippi River Delta, destroying thousands of acres of oyster beds and shrimp and crayfish grounds. But as luck would have it, the normal springtime breezes gave way to winds out of the north, which blew the slick out to sea instead of up the delta. As a result, the spill is believed to have done little lasting damage to the ecology of the area.

Oyster fishermen initially gave indication that they would cause quite a furor over the spill, but they were frightened into silence by public relations men who warned them that if they made too much noise, people would doubt the quality of their oysters, and in the long run they would be hurt more by the bad publicity than by the oil spill. So most of them remained quiet.

It is ironic that one of the strongest protests came from a U.S. senator from an interior state far removed from the Gulf Coast. Senator Gaylord Nelson, Democrat of Wisconsin, in a speech before the thirty-fourth annual meeting of the National Wildlife Federation held in Washington at the same time that the Chevron wells were polluting the Gulf, made an impassioned plea for sanity. Nelson proposed the establishment of a national oil resource trust to hold development of deposits under the ocean and in Alaska until foolproof drilling technology is developed.

"The present lack of knowledge about oil in the sea and in the Arctic makes it a criminal environmental folly to go on drilling new ocean wells and to span the Arctic with an eight-hundred-mile pipeline that could break and spew oil over the fragile tundra environment," Nelson said. "Yet by 1980, in a shocking invitation for trouble, we will be drilling three thousand to five thousand ocean oil wells worldwide each year. Untapped oil deposits under the sea and on federal lands in Alaska should be held unexploited in the National Trust until there is a national need for the oil, until environmental inventories have pinpointed all ecologically sensitive areas where drilling must never be allowed, and until we have the technology to contain major oil spills."

Nelson added this warning:

"Because of oil and other ocean pollution, scientists are now predicting the end of all productive life in the sea in fifty years or much less. In effect, we are slamming the door on the last chance for a livable world."

Interior Secretary Hickel met Nelson less than halfway when he proclaimed the Gulf spill a "disaster," adding that "It never should have happened."

On May 5, some thirty-five days after the last well was capped, Chevron was indicted for failure to install and maintain storm chokes or similar safety shutoff devices on ninety offshore oil wells. Federal prosecutors listed an astonishing total of nine hundred counts against Chevron, a subsidiary of Standard Oil of California, one of the largest oil companies in the world.

Storm chokes are mechanical devices in the wells that shut off the flow if the automatic platform at the surface is damaged by a hurricane or other means. If they had been installed, Hickel said, the oil spill would not have happened.

Public officials in Louisiana immediately came to the defense of Chevron. Russell Long must have been proud of the performance of his fellow public servants.

Governor John J. McKeithen, who had defended the oil industry from the start, let it be known prior to the indictments that he wanted to testify before the federal grand jury so that he could tell the jurors what a splendid job Chevron did in cleaning up the spill. He also conferred with Vice President Spiro Agnew in an attempt to convince Agnew to bring pressure against Hickel to resume the sale of offshore oil leases.

Hickel had suspended the sale of offshore oil leases following the Santa Barbara disaster, and that suspension was still in effect when Chevron's wells erupted more than a year later. The suspension, according to Louisiana Lieutenant Governor C. C. Aycock, was "disastrous."

Louisiana's attorney general, Jack P. F. Gremillion, the state's top legal watchdog, also came to the defense of Chevron, in spite of the fact that there was considerable evidence that the spill had been caused by gross negligence—the failure to install storm chokes. Gremillion called the oil slick "an act of God."

The case against Chevron was the first of its kind ever filed under the Outer Continental Shelf Lands Act, which was seventeen years old at the time of the Gulf spill. Chevron ultimately pleaded no contest to five hundred of the nine hundred counts, and the other 400 were dropped. Judge Alvin B. Rubin imposed a fine of two thousand dollars on each of the five hundred counts, totaling one million dollars.

Several months later, Shell Oil Company, Continental Oil Company, and Union Oil Company were cited for failing to install safety devices on seventy-four offshore oil wells in the Gulf. Shell was cited for 170 separate offenses on forty wells, Continental for 121 on twenty-six wells, and Union for twelve on eight wells. Each offense is punishable by a maximum fine of two thousand dollars.

All of this would seem to indicate that the federal government has finally recognized its responsibility and is ready to clamp down on the oil industry, the world's biggest polluter. But there is disturbing evidence that this is not so, that the government's few positive actions are offset by behind-the-scenes negotiations with the industry.

One indication that the country had been moving in the right direction came on January 1, 1970, when as his first official act of the new decade President Nixon signed into law the National Environmental Policy Act, which established the Council on Environmental Quality.

"I have charged the council with coordinating all environmental quality programs and with making a thorough review of all other federal programs which affect the environment," Nixon said in the "President's Message" preceding the council's first annual report. He went on to say:

"Federal agencies are now required to file with the Council

and the public a statement setting out in detail the environmental implications of all proposals for legislation and for other major activities with a significant environmental impact. With the help of this provision, I intend to ensure that environmental considerations are taken into account at the earliest possible stage of the decision-making process."

Toward the end of his message, the President had this to say about the environment:

"In dealing with the environment we must learn not how to master nature but how to master ourselves, our institutions, and our technology. We must achieve a new awareness of our dependence on our surroundings and on the natural systems which support all life, but awareness must be coupled with a full realization of our enormous capability to alter the surroundings. Nowhere is this capability greater than in the United States, and this country must lead the way in showing that our human and technological resources can be devoted to a better life and an improved environment for ourselves and our inheritors on this planet.

"Our environmental problems are very serious, indeed urgent, but they do not justify either panic or hysteria. The problems are highly complex, and their resolution will require rational, systematic approaches, hard work and patience. There must be a *national* commitment and a *rational* commitment [italics his].

"The newly aroused concern with our natural environment embraces old and young alike, in all walks of life. For the young, it has a special urgency. They know that it involves not only our own lives now but the future of mankind. For their parents, it has a special poignance—because ours is the first generation to feel the pangs of concern for the environmental legacy we leave to our children.

"At the heart of this concern for the environment lies our concern for the human condition: For the welfare of man himself, now and in the future. As we look ahead to the end of this new decade of heightened environmental awareness, therefore, we should set ourselves a higher goal than merely remedying the damage wrought in decades past. We should strive for an environment that not only sustains life but enriches life, harmonizing the works of man and nature for the greater good of all."

Those are stirring words.

Later that year, while the print was still wet on the President's message, Secretary Hickel journeyed all the way to Houston, Texas, in an unsuccessful attempt to help Representative George Bush win a seat in the U. S. Senate. Hickel spoke during a one-hundred-dollar-a-plate banquet, attended heavily by members of Houston's enormous oil enterprises.

Standing before the large audience, Hickel announced that the federal government would sell oil and gas leases on 593,-000 more acres of the Gulf of Mexico, thus ending the nineteen-month moratorium. The Secretary received a warm round of applause.

Later, Hickel admitted that he had neglected to consult the Council on Environmental Quality.

The guidelines of the council call for thirty-day prior notice of any major decision affecting the environment. The purpose of the rule is to give the council a chance to study proposed governmental actions and to confer with appropriate officials to make certain the action does not pose a threat to the environment.

A spokesman for Hickel conceded that the council's guidelines were ignored, but he said, "That's just what they are—guidelines. There's nothing legally binding about them."

Following the Houston fiasco, the Nixon Administration succeeded in gathering its scattered antipollution forces under a single command, the unified Environmental Protection Agency (EPA). The agency is designed to serve as the enforcing arm of the government's attack on pollution.

The agency is independent of any cabinet office, similar to NASA and the AEC. According to the first report of the Council on Environmental Quality, EPA's main role is to establish and enforce standards, monitor and analyze the environment, conduct research and demonstrations, and assist state and local government pollution control programs. The agency combines programs formerly housed in five separate federal departments, including the Federal Water Quality Administration, the National Air Pollution Control Administration, and several programs dealing with solid waste management, radiation hazards, and pesticides. The EPA's total budget approaches 1.4 billion dollars, and it employs almost six thousand persons.

One of the most disturbing developments in the nationwide fight to save the environment came on November 25, 1970. Secretary Hickel had scheduled a meeting at the White House with George P. Shultz, head of the Office of Management and Budget, to discuss the coming fiscal year. He arrived at Shultz' White House office at 4:45 P.M., but Shultz was not there. He talked for a while with subordinates, and a short time later a White House staffer approached Hickel with word that the President wanted to see him. Hickel went to the Oval Office, where he found Nixon waiting with one of his top aides, John D. Ehrlichman, chief of the Domestic Affairs Council.

During a brief, tense exchange, Hickel learned what it feels like to be fired by the President of the United States.

A short time later, Hickel appeared before a small group of reporters at the Interior Department. Choked with emotion, he said:

"The President personally terminated me about two hours ago. There's really nothing I can say at this time to help the situation or to hurt it. Given the hostility toward me when I first arrived and some of those incredible decisions I had to make immediately afterward and trying to do a job for the President and all Americans and somehow survive as an individual—I had to do it my way."

The short saga of Wally Hickel had come to an end. A self-made millionaire, he had climbed all the way to the highest echelons of power. A former pugilist, he had fought the only way he knew how: with blows to the gut and undercuts in the clinches, but always in the center of the ring.

The political demise of Hickel was mourned by conservationists across the country, and particularly in Santa Barbara. It was true that he had not always been in their corner, and there were many times when his performance had been disappointing, but he had done more than any other Nixon appointee to help curb the destruction of planet Earth. As he said, he did it his way, and his way was not accepted in the polished circles of diplomacy in Washington, where Hickel's sharp corners caused gross discomfort.

Hickel was fired because he made enemies out of the wrong people, not the least of whom was the President himself. Nixon never forgave Hickel for a letter protesting his attitudes toward young people, which somehow leaked to the press. And there were many times when the Alaskan proved to be an embarrassment to the Administration, including his failure to work through the Council on Environmental Quality in the decision to sell more leases in the Gulf of Mexico.

Four days after Hickel won reluctant confirmation from the U. S. Senate in 1969, the Santa Barbara Channel belched black crude oil into the sea. Hickel was caught in a rising tide of public concern over the environment, and he seemed to recognize before he was fired that his performance had not fully satisfied anyone.

His thoughts were revealed the night before his exit from power during a taped interview with CBS newsman Mike Wallace.

"I had to walk that thin line. I obviously wasn't owned by the oil industry or owned by the conservationists. I probably wasn't owned by anybody, and that's probably the problem. I've always believed that if you do a good job for all the people in the country, then you do a good job for the President. And I think that was what I was supposed to do. And so I'll say that I'm going to do the best I can, but if I go away, I'm going away with an arrow in my heart, and not a bullet in my back."

What Hickel failed to realize was that most Americans want to build a better world, but they do not want to be uncomfortable during the process. And thus it was that from the start Wally Hickel was a man with an Achilles heel—he had an uncomfortable conscience, and he tried to make others uncomfortable, too.

It has been a long, long time since the floor of the Santa Barbara Channel ruptured. What has it all come to?

In the years since the blowout, much has been said, and little has been done.

The year of 1970 was proclaimed as the Year of the Environment all across the nation, and legislators joined the fight with stirring speeches and impassioned press releases. Literally thousands of bills were introduced in state legislatures and the U. S. Congress dealing with the environment. Few states succeeded in getting more than two or three measures passed, and the federal record was even worse.

There have been failures, but there have also been successes; more, perhaps, than at any other time in this nation's history. One of the most significant success stories unfolded on Santa Barbara's own doorstep in a subdivision of Los Angeles, known as Pacific Palisades. Despite strong protests from residents of the area, the city of Los Angeles on July 24, 1970, awarded an exploratory drilling permit to Occidental Petroleum Corporation for a two-acre parcel at the foot of a bluff, just across Pacific Coast Highway from Will Rogers State Beach. Scores of homes were located on top of the Palisades, the scene of numerous landslides. In 1958, a state highway engineer, standing at the foot of the bluff, pronounced it safe. Moments later, he was killed when he was buried beneath tons of mud. The bluff itself was so unstable that the state refused to permit persons to park their cars at its base. Will Rogers State Beach is one of the most popular parks in Southern California, and a major slide could have claimed the lives of people at the foot of the bluff, as well as those in the homes at the top. But to the astonishment of nearly everyone, city zoning administrator Rowland A. Rudser approved the exploratory permit, thus endangering the lives and property of many.

Residents of the area immediately formed No Oil, Inc., a one-purpose organization patterned after GOO! Their goal was singular: to win a reversal of Rudser's ruling. But the reversal would have to come from the Board of Zoning Appeals, which had not turned down a core hole permit in its entire history.

Occidental launched a massive propaganda campaign, claiming that "an overwhelming majority" of property owners within the "area of interest" were in favor of the drilling. No Oil immediately conducted a survey of 920 homes in the immediate neighborhood. The survey was answered by 628 residents. Nearly 90 percent of the respondents, a total of 551 people, opposed any oil exploration. As it turned out, Occidental's "overwhelming majority" included businesses and individuals who owned vast areas of unimproved land, some of which probably could not be developed because of the unstable hills. They favored the drilling because they would have received a royalty from the oil company.

No Oil, Inc., took the case before the county grand jury, which on August 28, 1970, issued a statement urging the Board of Zoning Appeals to kill the exploratory permit.

"It is tragic both for the residents and the millions of people who use Will Rogers State Beach to face the possibility of the ugly sight, sound and smell of oil drilling," the statement said. It added that "The physical disruption of terrain which already is unstable geologically is pollution of the highest order. The 1970 Los Angeles County Grand Jury supports the stand of No Oil, Inc., against all oil exploration and drilling in the Pacific Palisades."

Los Angeles Mayor Sam Yorty, a long-time friend of Occidental President Armand Hammer, denounced the grand jury for interceding and suggested that the jurors pay more attention to crime and less to Occidental.

In spite of the opposition, No Oil, Inc. won the battle to save the Palisades. On September 15, after an eight-hour hearing, the Board of Zoning Appeals unanimously reversed the exploratory drilling permit.

Yorty once again dashed to the forefront, this time to denounce the appeals board. The board, Yorty suggested, had been subjected to "unethical tactics" by residents who applied political pressure. He refused to accept the old axiom that "what's good for the goose is good for the gander."

The people won at Pacific Palisades, just as they have won in numerous environmental battles across the nation. There seems little doubt that the age of the environment has at long last arrived, and although many feared that the public would soon grow weary and shift its attention to other things, that does not seem to be the case. If anything, public hostility against the polluters has increased, and there is no reason to believe that life will ever be quite as free-and-easy as it once was for those who would tread thoughtlessly across mother Earth.

There is some consolation in that for the people of Santa Barbara. Even if it means they won the war, but lost the battle.

Part
Two

7

Oil is so much a part of our lives today that it is almost impossible to imagine a time when it was not regarded as a valuable commodity. Yet just a little over a century ago crude oil was usually more of a nuisance than a blessing. It spoiled streams, ruined water wells, and—God forgive—even polluted the sea near the Santa Barbara mission. Nobody had figured out what to do with it since the Indians quit using it as warpaint. It seems almost incredible that oil could have risen from that ignoble beginning to one of the most valuable of all natural resources. Without petroleum and its wide range of products the industrial world of today would screech to a halt. People have found that they cannot get along without it, but they cannot always find it where they want it. Sometimes, in order to get it, they have had to pay a tremendous price, and not always in money.

Over the years, the petroleum industry has learned how to live with its own peculiarities. It has learned, for example, how to deal with unstable governments in some of the obscure little countries that are rich with oil. Since the industry's entire profit system begins with getting the oil out of the ground, it has learned how to deal with people who would block or impede its actions. In short, the oil industry has learned how to live in a world that sometimes hates it but always needs it. That kind of thing makes fighters out of people, and, if human traits can be transferred to industries, it would have to be said that above all else the oil industry is a fighter.

The rapid rise of what is now the world's biggest and most

powerful business has not been without problems. There are more rogues than knights in the history of the oil industry, and it is one of those disturbing paradoxes of nature that the rogues, in the long run, have done more good than the knights. They gave the business the power and the guts to do what had to be done, and they—sometimes unscrupulously —tied the loose ends of a neophyte industry into corporations of great power and tremendous resources.

How and why this all came about helps explain why the oil industry operates the way it does today.

Scientists first began to realize the potential of oil more than a century ago, in the middle 1800s. They were able to show, for instance, that if oil was properly refined it served even better than coal oil as a fuel for lamps. The problem was that nobody was able to come up with enough crude oil to make such operations worthwhile.

Enterprising men in several areas of the world began struggling with that problem at about the same time. Some theorized that since oil sometimes polluted water wells, it might be possible to drill for oil just as they drilled for water. They figured that they could drill in an area that was known to have oil, such as a natural seep, and stand a good chance of finding a considerable quantity.

Of all those who tried, only one is remembered. His name was Edwin L. Drake, a bearded drifter who had moved from job to job throughout his life, and who liked to call himself "colonel," although he had never been in the Army. Drake entered the picture in 1859, when he showed up on a farm near Titusville, Pennsylvania, and introduced himself to the owner, a young New York lawyer by the name of George H. Bissell. Bissell had purchased the farm because a crude oil sample found there had been used successfully in several experiments at Dartmouth. He had hoped to market the crude, but he soon ran into problems. He did not have much money, and he did not know how to get the oil out of the ground.

Drake had somehow managed to save a little capital and

he offered to put up this money in return for a cut of the take. Bissell accepted, and in the summer of 1859 the farm sprouted the country's first oil derrick, which was quickly dubbed by the locals as "Drake's Folly." They quit laughing on August 27 when oil was struck at a little over sixty-nine feet. The oil just oozed to the surface under its own momentum, and in a few days it was producing thirty barrels a day. The oil sold to coal oil dealers for twenty dollars a barrel.

Titusville immediately took on the appearance of a boom town, with some farms changing hands several times a day. Wells sprang up across the Pennsylvania landscape, and history took an unalterable turn. Speculators paid huge sums for farms, and then tried to pump the oil out as fast as possible in an attempt to regain their investment. In a short time, the market was flooded and the price of crude oil plunged. Within a few years, the price reached an all-time low of ten cents a barrel.

It was there, not far from Drake's Folly, that the new industry learned one of its most valuable lessons: A little oil is worth a lot, but too much oil is worth little. In time, the market leveled off at a profitable price—one of the Titusville wells earned 1.5 million dollars for a local storekeeper—but somewhere along the way a lot of people went broke and a lot of companies flopped. One of them was Bissell's, and Drake soon found himself out of a job, again. He worked for a while as the justice of the peace in Titusville, but he died in 1880 as a pauper.

In the wake of Titusville, scores of small companies were founded, and some succeeded. But none had the resources or the capability to handle the valuable new commodity known as oil. They either produced too much, or too little, and they knifed each other in the back so many times that it appeared for a while that all would lose. What the industry needed was a giant of a man who could pull the loose ends together, and history provided such a man.

His name was John D. Rockefeller, and he became one of the most controversial and legendary figures in United States history. Rockefeller was born on July 8, 1839, the son of a ne'er-do-well who once advertised himself as "Dr. William A. Rockefeller, the Celebrated Cancer Specialist." John's mother was a religious woman, and when her son was fifteen years old he became a member of the Erie Street Baptist Church in Cleveland. His religion meant a great deal to him, and over the years it continued to play a major role in his life.

As the years passed, John grew into manhood, carrying the virtues of his youth with him. He was a generous man, giving a substantial share of his earnings to those who were less fortunate. And he soon developed a keen business sense, combining the traditional American virtues of thrift, hard work, and free enterprise. He entered a partnership in 1959 with an Englishman, Maurice Clark, forming the commission agency of Clark and Rockefeller. One of the products they handled was kerosene, and in the early 1860s they took on another partner, Samuel Andrews, who had the reputation of being able to get more kerosene out of a barrel of crude oil than anyone else. They established a small refinery, and by 1865 it was the biggest in Cleveland.

Early that year, Clark and Rockefeller reached a disagreement over the future of their business. Rockefeller wanted to expand the refinery, but Clark did not want to borrow the money required for such a venture. They finally parted, after Rockefeller borrowed 72,500 dollars, which he gave to Clark along with his share of the agency. In exchange, Rockefeller received Clark's share of the refinery.

Although he was only twenty-six, a new Rockefeller had begun to emerge, and the germ of a bold plan had started to form. There were more losers than winners in the oil business, mainly because of the unstable nature of the business itself. This was especially true on the production end. It seemed that every time the market began to stabilize, some joker would discover a new oil field and flood the market. Prices dropped, and millionaires who had spread themselves too thin became paupers overnight. No one was big enough to do anything about it, and there appeared little chance that any of the hundreds of wildcatters would be willing to cooperate.

Rockefeller decided that only the middleman could introduce sanity to the oil business. Only the refineries could control the market, but in order to do so they would need the storage capability and the financial resources to carry them over the dry spells by capitalizing every time the prices dropped. Rockefeller knew that it would take a giant to do that, and he decided to become that man. Whether it was a conscious decision or not, Rockefeller resolved that he would dominate the oil business with all the ferocity and viciousness that such a scheme would require.

In 1867, Rockefeller invited a successful grain merchant, Henry M. Flagler, to join Andrews and himself in the refinery. Flagler was the son-in-law of Stephen V. Harkness, who had made a fortune by buying whiskey just before the start of the Civil War, and then selling it at an enormous profit after the imposition of special war taxes. Harkness became a silent partner in the refinery after contributing at least sixty thousand dollars.

Flagler was a tremendous businessman, and he proved a great asset to Rockefeller. At Flagler's suggestion, the firm issued stock, and on January 10, 1870, the Standard Oil Company was incorporated with Rockefeller as president. According to Rockefeller's own estimates, during the following year more than three-fourths of the oil refiners in the country lost money, and Standard moved to capitalize on that situation. The firm took over several smaller refineries in the Cleveland area, and by the end of the year Standard was probably the biggest refinery in the country.

One of Rockefeller's chief goals was to become big enough to deal with the railroads. Communities and industries all across the nation lived and died by the whims of railroad barons who controlled the country's lifelines. Communities and companies that refused to play ball and balked at the rates demanded by the dictators of the rails simply died from lack of nourishment.

Rockefeller knew the game well. But he also knew the other side. Unlike other big companies, the railroads had never been able to pull together, frequently engaging in price wars over the bigger markets. The only way to win, Rockefeller knew, was to become big enough to force the railroads to deal on his terms. But before he got a chance to approach the railroads, the railroads came to him.

The three main oil lines, the Pennsylvania, the Erie, and the New York Central, recognized that price wars on shipping rates were damaging them more than anyone else, so they called on Rockefeller with a plan of their own.

The railroad executives wanted the thirteen largest refineries to form an association. The three railroads would do the same. Each association would offer special terms to the other, thus stamping out the competition. Everybody would realize a healthy profit, and the consumers far down the line would pay the bill. It was the sort of plan that appealed to Rockefeller, although he had doubts that so many companies could cooperate successfully. But he agreed, and the thirteen refineries joined together under the euphemistic name of the South Improvement Company.

Under the plan, members of the South Improvement Company would receive a discount on their shipments. In addition, they would receive a discount for every barrel of oil shipped by competitors who were not members of the association. Thus the competitors not only were paying higher rates, they were subsidizing the members of the association with every barrel they shipped.

The plan might have worked, but the secret leaked out, and oilmen across the nation went into orbit. Demands for an investigation were sent to Congress; a petition ninety-three feet long called for the construction of a pipeline to break the railroads' monopoly; and one thousand men were ready to march on the Pennsylvania capital. The refineries excluded from the association launched an embargo against the conspirators, and the oil industry encountered its first tidal wave of public hostility. The refiners finally admitted during a congressional investigation that the purpose of their plot had been to raise prices.

Rockefeller wanted to continue with the plan in spite of the public outrage, but the others backed out. They might have been better off if they had played ball. The industry was on the brink of bankruptcy, and Rockefeller decided to go it alone. At that time, Standard accounted for between 10 and 20 percent of the nation's refining capacity. But by 1879, Rockefeller controlled something like 90 percent, and it became painfully apparent that by comparison the South Improvement Company had been child's play.

Over the years, refineries had sprouted up like Christmas trees in December, and the predictable result was too much oil. Many of the owners had spread themselves too thin, expecting the demand to rise again, but it just did not happen that way. The price of oil continued to plunge, and in 1873 the United States was hit by a major recession. The future appeared bleak, indeed.

It was little wonder that owners were willing to sell to Rockefeller, even at a considerable loss, rather than go on losing money in a venture that appeared hopeless. Rockefeller was the only one willing to buy up the refineries, and he was the only one with the resources to establish equilibrium within the market. Most owners were easily convinced. Those who held out were pressured into accepting, sometimes through the promise of a good job with Standard. Those who insisted on fighting soon learned that it was not worth the effort. Rockefeller used his growing power to force the railroads to charge the holdouts higher rates, and in time they came around, sometimes on the brink of bankruptcy. One such company employed Rockefeller's own elder brother, Frank, who told a congressional committee that his brother had made it clear that if they did not give in they would be smashed.

One of the reasons for Rockefeller's success was the refining skill of Sam Andrews, who, unlike others in the business, tried to convert the various by-products of the refining process into useful materials. He used the gasoline as fuel to heat the stills in the refinery, oil was marketed for lubricating purposes, and he consistently managed to derive the maximum value from the raw materials. Other refiners who were not as visionary as Andrews just dumped the by-products into nearby rivers, and industry has been doing that in varying degrees ever since.

Rockefeller's growing power both frightened and pleased railroad executives. They were happy to see some stability coming to the market, but they were afraid that in the end Rockefeller would undercut them, just as he had everyone else. As it turned out, their fears were well founded.

One man who saw the danger was Joseph D. Potts, head of the Empire Transportation Company. In those days, wells were tied together by a series of crude pipelines laid on the surface. The pipelines were not designed to carry the oil over long distances, but they were vital in getting the oil from the wells to the railhead. Potts reasoned that if he could control the pipelines, he could control Rockefeller, since Standard would have to go through him to move its oil from the fields to the refinery. But Rockefeller learned of the plan and began buying the remaining pipelines.

The result was a long, bitter battle. Empire prospered, in spite of Standard's strength, but in 1877 fate stepped in on Rockefeller's side. Empire was a subsidiary of the Pennsylvania Railroad, and 1877 was one of the most agonizing years in the history of the railroads.

In April of that year a bitter rate war broke out among the eastern railroads, affecting passenger as well as freight fares, and in the summer employees went out on strike. It was a fiercely bitter dispute, culminating with a bloody clash between strikers and police in Pittsburgh. Police opened fire, killing twenty-five men. Elsewhere, looting and destruction took place around the clock.

When it was all over, many of the railroad companies had been severely crippled. The Pennsylvania line had lost more than one hundred locomotives and fifteen hundred passenger and freight cars. The only way out was to sell, and Standard bought out all of Empire's oil interests for 3.4 million dollars cash. Rockefeller continued his acquisitions, and by the end of the year virtually no oil anywhere in the country moved from the wells to the railroads without his permission.

Rockefeller then closed in for the kill. Since he controlled both the oil industry and the railroads, he was able to carry out the aborted plan of the South Improvement Company, demanding lower rates for his own oil, plus a discount for oil shipped by his few remaining competitors. It was a dastardly scheme, and howls of protest from those who were caught in Rockefeller's net soon attracted attention. In general, the government was hesitant to act, but the public's outrage was too strong to ignore. It had come to light that independent producers had to pay $1.44 a barrel to send their oil from Titusville to New York, but Standard was charged only eighty cents. The company pocketed the difference. It was obvious that only the consumer could lose from such an arrangement, and Rockefeller had become the source of widespread public concern.

Rockefeller ignored the fact that the American people were beginning to recognize him as Public Enemy No. 1, and he pushed on. He was troubled by a new threat. A small group of producers had decided to fight back with a bold plan. They wanted to build a pipeline over the Allegheny Mountains to the coast, thus eliminating the railroads entirely. It was a brazen idea, and most people thought it would not work. Pipelines had never been used to carry oil more than a few miles, and in order to reach the coast the pipeline would have to cross the Alleghenys at twenty-six hundred feet. To do this seemingly impossible task, the new group—which had organized under the name of the Tidewater Pipe Company—turned to General Herman Haupt, a famed civil engineer with a reputation for doing the impossible.

Rockefeller scoffed at the proposal, although as a precaution he bought tracts of land lying across the route he thought the pipeline would have to follow. Against these impossible odds, Haupt set out to build the pipeline. He managed to wind the pipe around Rockefeller's tracts, but the odds were still heavily against Haupt. In the winter, horse-drawn carts hauled the supplies for thirty miles through snow-covered passes. In the summer, before the pipelane was buried, scorching heat made it twist around like a giant snake, knocking down trees. It seemed impossible, but on May 28, 1879, oil began flowing through Haupt's pipeline.

The line reduced the cost of transporting a barrel of oil to the coast from forty cents to seventeen cents, and Rockefeller knew he was in for a fight. The railroads dropped their fares to ten cents, but it would never be the same again. Rockefeller began building his own pipelines, and at the same time he tried to force Tidewater to knuckle under.

By the fall of 1883, Standard owned many pipelines itself, and it had managed to keep Tidewater in the courts in expensive legal battles for prolonged periods. The owners of Tidewater wanted to hold out, but Rockefeller came around with one of his generous offers, and they knew that in the long run they would lose anyway. So they sold out to Standard, and the rates shot up to forty-five cents a barrel. Rockefeller was stronger than ever.

During this period Rockefeller embarked on a reorganization of his company that was to have a profound impact upon American business. Standard had become a nationwide company, but in those days the laws governing companies in the various states had not kept pace with industrial development. Standard's wide-flung operations had become unwieldy with the various laws in the different states. As an Ohio corporation, it was illegal for Standard to own companies in other states. To get around this, stock in the other companies was consigned to a company officer within the state, and he in effect functioned as the owner. This loose arrangement worked, but it lacked the tight corporate control that Rockefeller wanted. So he created the Standard Oil Trust, the first of the great nationwide holding companies. On January 2, 1882, Rockefeller established his new headquarters in New York in a ten-story building at the site of a house

that once belonged to Alexander Hamilton. Thus it was
that the same plot of land accommodated Hamilton, who
championed the idea of America as a great industrial nation,
and, years later, Rockefeller, who fulfilled that dream.

The trust company gave Rockefeller the control he had
wanted over his own interests. Standard organized separate
companies in each of the states, all subject to control by a
single board of trustees. In 1892, the Ohio Supreme Court
ruled that the trust company violated Standard's original
charter, since most of the trustees did not live in the state, so
the firm reorganized as Standard Oil Company of New Jersey,
which is today the largest oil company in the world.

Over the years Standard continued to prosper from a position of strength. The company never became a monopoly,
with 10 to 20 percent of the nation's oil interests owned by
smaller, independent firms. It was not worth the expense to
stamp them out, so, as long as they stayed in their own little
corners and did not try to grow too large, they were allowed
to survive. But as soon as any company tried to cut in on
Standard's market, it was smashed through Rockefeller's tight
control over the pipelines, the railroads, and the retail outlets.

There were a few attempts to establish new pipelines, but
Rockefeller blocked most by buying tracts of land across the
proposed route. In other cases, he ordered the railroads to
block the line by denying permission to tunnel under their
tracks. The only man who succeeded was William Larimer
Mellon, the twenty-three-year-old scion of the Pittsburgh
banking family. Mellon won a court order that permitted him
to lay a line across Pennsylvania, regardless of whose land or
whose tracks he had to cross. However, the Pennsylvania Railroad put up a costly legal fight, and on several occasions
gangs ripped up part of the pipeline. But young Mellon kept
at it, and the project was completed in 1892 at a cost of more
than one million dollars. A short time later, he sold out to
Rockefeller for 2.5 million dollars.

Throughout his climb to power, Rockefeller was a man of
contrasts. Regardless of his immense personal wealth, he re-

mained a man of relatively simple tastes. He gave away more than five hundred million dollars during his lifetime, emerging as one of the nation's greatest philanthropists. But in his business life he never deviated from his obsession for power, and he remained a ruthless, vicious adversary. He never seemed to recognize the conflicts between his personal and his corporate lives.

As he himself admitted, he had not set out to make a fortune. Money, to Rockefeller, was a by-product of power and a result of his success in building the richest and most powerful company in the entire world. In the end, he was extremely pleased that he had been the one to bring order out of chaos in the oil industry. But he did more than that. He gave the industry its birthright, and although the Rockefeller empire was doomed, he had established the pattern for the years ahead. Others had learned his ways well, and as the years passed, they would apply Rockefeller stratagems whenever and wherever they were needed.

As irony would have it, one of the men who helped bring about the decline of Standard was the sort of fellow Rockefeller never would have considered a threat. Patillo Higgins was a one-armed former lumberjack who had convinced himself that there was oil in Texas. He labored for ten years near the city of Beaumont to prove his point, spending more than thirty thousand dollars of his own money. But Higgins finally was forced to give up the fight. Broke, but still convinced that oil would be found in Texas, Higgins convinced Anthony Lucas, a former captain in the Austrian Navy, to take over the project. But Lucas, too, spent all of his money and was forced to sell to a group backed by the Mellon family.

Finally, on January 10, 1901, Texas yielded up her riches with an explosion heard for miles around, followed by a gusher several hundred feet high. They called the well Spindletop, and to this day it remains the most famous oil well in history.

The discovery changed the complexion of the oil industry overnight, bringing in new blood and new money to challenge

Rockefeller's forces. Although he had sold out to the Mellons, Lucas enjoyed some of the success by retaining a small stake in the venture. But Higgins faded into obscurity, and he spent the rest of his life wandering over the state looking for another strike. He never found it, and he died in 1955, at the age of 92, tired, lonely, forgotten, and broke.

The Texas strike was unlike anything the world had seen before. In one year the first Spindletop well alone produced as much oil as thirty-seven thousand wells in the eastern states. The riches gave rise to several strong companies, including the Mellon firm, now known as Gulf, and the Texas Company, now known as Texaco. Today both rank among the largest companies in the world.

Spindletop's timing was against Rockefeller. The discovery coincided with a major transformation within the oil industry and the international marketplace. The age of the automobile had dawned, and gasoline rapidly replaced kerosene as the major product of the refining process. Standard's executives belonged to another age, and they were unable to adapt to the changing world as quickly as the newer, more energetic companies in Texas. In addition, Standard was having its share of legal problems, and much of the company's time, money, and energy was tied up in the courts.

Rockefeller's problems were intensified by a change in public attitudes. People were beginning to realize that unlimited economic power could easily lead to unlimited corruption. In 1889 the U. S. Congress passed the Sherman Act to "declare unlawful, trusts and combinations in restraint of trade, and production." The matter greatly troubled Theodore Roosevelt, who became President on September 14, 1901, following the assassination of William McKinley. As the scion of a wealthy family, Roosevelt understood that money meant power, and feared that powerful businessmen could someday preside over elected officials the way medieval barons had ruled the kings of England. He decided to do something about it. Teddy Roosevelt embodied a new age in American politics: the age of reform. He strengthened government controls over big business through reinforcing the Interstate Commerce Commission, which launched trust-busting suits against many major corporations. Roosevelt also backed the passage of the Meat Inspection Act and the Pure Food and Drugs Act.

Rockefeller's actions probably had been no worse than those of other powerful businessmen of that troubled era, but he was by far the best known, and he thus became the favorite target for the reformers. More than twenty state governments sued to evict Standard from their territories between the years of 1904 and 1909. But the most important of all the legal actions was a federal suit in Missouri aimed at forcing Standard to break up its nationwide trust company. In 1909, Standard lost. It appealed, but on May 15, 1911, the U. S. Supreme Court ordered the company to get rid of its major subsidiaries within six months. The company was broken into more than thirty pieces, each independent of the others.

An era was coming to an end. Rockefeller, seventy-two, resigned from the presidency and watched his empire collapse. He lived for another twenty-six years, and it was during that period that he became one of the greatest philanthropists of all time. He gave away more than half a billion dollars, but when he died in 1937 his personal fortune was still worth over twenty-six million dollars. He had completely divorced himself from his company, retaining only one share for sentimental reasons.

Actually, Standard's empire was in trouble even before Spindletop, but few people recognized it at that time. It began on the other side of the world at Baku in far-off Russia, where oil had been seeping to the surface for thousands of years. In 1873, the Czarist regime finally allowed prospectors into the area, and among the first to arrive were the Nobel brothers, Ludwig, Robert, and Alfred. Their father had invented torpedo boats, Ludwig and Robert had built the St. Petersburg dockyards, and Alfred, who later established the Nobel prizes, had invented dynamite. By applying Rockefeller's techniques, the inventive Nobel brothers soon established a strong toehold in the area, but the growth and production of Russia's oil industry was so great that numerous overlords soon reigned over private empires. They surrounded themselves with wasteful extravagance, which undoubtedly played a major role in the shaping of Russia's modern personality. Stories have it that one owner built his storage tanks out of platinum, while another built his palace out of gold plate. The contrast between the rich and the poor was appalling, and it is little wonder that Baku produced some of Russia's most prominent leaders, including Joseph Stalin.

Russian oil soon flooded Europe, and although Standard made a serious effort, it was unable to gain the control over the foreign market that it enjoyed in the United States. Several companies continued to expand, particularly in Europe. Finally, in 1907, two of Europe's largest companies—Henri Deterding's Royal Dutch and Marcus Samuel's Shell—merged into the Royal Dutch Shell Group. The new company was large enough to challenge Standard on its own terms.

The merger also created an international counterpart to Rockefeller in the form of Henri Deterding, who had dropped out of school at the age of sixteen. He became a bank clerk, and finally, out of boredom, turned to oil. The two men were of widely differing characters. Whereas Rockefeller was a somber man whose private life revolved around his family and his church, Deterding was a flamboyant playboy who enjoyed bestowing lavish gifts on beautiful women, and who traveled between his many homes in plush, private trains. But both men were driven by a deep-rooted passion for success in their business lives, and Deterding worked as hard as he played. To him, the oil business was more of a sport than anything else; he loved the sense of competition, and he savored the triumphs of a winner. Unlike Rockefeller, Deterding never seemed to want to establish a monopoly on the international oil business. Indeed, he seemed to long for competition, although he disapproved of the price-cutting rate wars that had typified Standard's operations in the United States. Deterding figured that business should be competitive, but orderly and profitable.

In a real sense, Deterding was more sophisticated than Rockefeller. Instead of smashing his competition, he chose to join with it in secret agreements, and Deterding gave the industry a whole new dimension.

Meanwhile, another man entered the picture, and it was he—Calouste Sarkis Gulbenkian—who was to carry Deterding's theories to perfection. In the later 1800s the German government was constructing a railroad from Berlin to Baghdad, which meant that the tracks had to cross Mesopotamia. Along with their right-of-way, the Germans also acquired mineral rights for twenty kilometers along both sides of the projected rails. But while the Germans were laying the tracks, they became more excited about something else. They had discovered natural seeps along the tracks. The sultan became suspicious over the excitement, and his advisers searched for someone who could unravel the mystery. They turned to Gulbenkian, who had achieved an international reputation although he was only twenty-one years old. The young Armenian had traveled widely, and he understood the oil business surprisingly well. Gulbenkian explained the value of the oil to his country's leaders, and he immediately learned a valuable lesson that was to guide him throughout an astonishing career. Gulbenkian's lesson: Information is a valuable commodity; the man who tells his superiors something they did not know before stands to gain financially, but only if they think he knows more than he has told them.

Since he had answered all their questions, Gulbenkian was sent on his way with nothing more than a polite word of "thanks," and he resolved that things would be different in the future.

Germany's mineral rights were revoked, but the government did nothing about the oil. Although he did not know it at the time, the sultan was sitting on one of the richest oil fields in the world, and in the years ahead the Middle East deposits would change the complexion of the world. Gulbenkian somehow sensed the future. He vowed that somehow he would be part of it.

During the next few years, Gulbenkian ingratiated himself with the captains of the oil industry—including Deterding—and he served in various advisory capacities with a number of governments. There is little doubt that over the years he became the foremost expert on the operational aspects of the different oil companies, and he perhaps understood the subtleties of the industry better than anyone else in the world.

In 1910, three London financiers established the National Bank of Turkey. One of the men they picked to serve on the board of directors was Calouste Gulbenkian. From that position, Gulbenkian felt he could launch a drive toward his lifelong ambition—to do something about the oil in Mesopotamia. After several legal obstacles and months of negotiations, the Turkish Petroleum Company was formed in an amalgamation of various enterprises, including Shell, the Deutsche Bank, and the Anglo-Persian Oil Company. Because of his efforts, and because he knew the delicate legal framework under which the new company was organized, Gulbenkian received a 5 percent interest in the new firm. From that point on, he was known throughout the world as Mr. Five Percent.

Gulbenkian's dream was interrupted by World War I. Later, when the opportunity to develop the oil fields in the Middle East again materialized, the world had changed. The Turkish Petroleum Company was organized again, but this time Germany was dropped from the plan. The shareholders in the new company were Shell, Compagnie Française des Petroles of France, Anglo-Persian of Great Britain, and an American group of seven companies headed by Jersey Standard. Each of the four owned 23¾ percent of the company. The rest went to Gulbenkian to make up his 5 percent.

Gulbenkian's role is still one of the great mysteries of the oil industry. He invested little of his own money, yet he consistently walked away from the negotiating table with a comfortable piece of the action. He accomplished this through his intimate knowledge of each company, and through the experiences he gathered over the course of a lifetime. When all else failed, he threatened to expose his adversaries in the courts, and they always came around, anxious to keep their secrets to themselves. From 1914 to 1953, Mr. Five Percent received several million dollars a year, partly as a reward for his services, and partly as a reward for keeping quiet. When he died in 1955, he took most of his secrets with him.

Gulbenkian's plan brought together three of the world's great powers—Great Britain, France, and the United States —in what was probably the best case of international price fixing in history. In October 1927, the French presented a map with a crude red line drawn around what was generally considered the Turkish Empire. The line encompassed nearly the entire Arabian peninsula, including Saudi Arabia, Iraq, Jordan, Syria, and Turkey. The result was the famed Red Line Agreement. Under the agreement, each of the five partners in the Turkish Petroleum Company pledged not to compete with the other partners. All actions by each company were subject to the approval of the other four.

The scheme gave each partner the power of veto over the actions of the others, thus eliminating any chance of competition. The plan bogged down for a while, partly because of efforts of the big four to cut off Gulbenkian's annoying 5 percent, but in the end he won and the agreement was signed. There is little reason to believe that anyone at that time anticipated the full impact of the future. The first drilling took place at Baba Gugur, near the Eternal Fires of Nebuchadnezzar's furnace. The engineers figured that the fires were fueled by a large deposit, but no one had expected the drama that unfolded on October 27, 1927. When the drill broke through the reservoir the oil roared out of the ground in a gusher so high it could be seen twelve miles away. The oil flowed out at the staggering rate of 12,500 tons a day, turning the countryside into a black sea. For the first time in recorded history, Nebuchadnezzar's furnace had to be put out because of fears of an explosion.

The oil field was one of the largest in the world, and it revolutionized the Middle East, just as it later helped to revolutionize the entire world. Iraq suddenly became the center of attention, and the Turkish Petroleum Company wisely changed its name to the Iraq Petroleum Company.

Gulbenkian's plan might have had a greater impact if it had not been for one major flaw. There was more oil in the Middle East than even he had dreamed of, and it did not all lie within the Red Line. Anticipating this, Gulf Oil, eager for a stake in the Middle East, entered into a joint agreement in 1933 with Anglo-Persian. The result was the Kuwait Oil Company, which won exploration rights from Kuwait's Sheikh Ahmad al Jabir al Sabah.

Oil discoveries in the tiny country defied the imagination. Today, it is estimated that no less than a sixth of the known world oil reserves are in Kuwait. The new discoveries greatly weakened the Red Line, but it survived until World War II, when its fate was sealed with the fall of France. After the war, France was so desperate for oil to help repair its wounds that it agreed to end the Red Line in exchange for a promise from the international oil industry that its interest in Iraq would be preserved and Iraqi fields would be developed quickly.

Eventually, it became clear that the winners in the Middle East were the American oil companies, who controlled most of the oil reserves throughout that promising area. But it is ironic that victory for the Americans came at a time when America needed more oil about as much as it needed another war. New discoveries in the United States, and the Great Depression, had set the stage for a disastrous market for oil and its various products. Prices dropped from $1.30 to five cents a barrel and, as fate would have it, the country where free enterprise and spirited competition had been regarded as the greatest of virtues gave way to rigid governmental controls as a means of helping the troubled industry.

For the first time, the federal government moved to eliminate imported oil, which was undermining the domestic market. The individual states also got into the act, setting up rigid production quotas as a means of cutting down on the surplus oil and thus raising the prices. In 1934, the U. S. Congress passed the "Hot Oil Act," which made it illegal to transport oil across state boundaries without approval.

Most of the emergency provisions adopted during those troubled days are still in effect. The states still regulate the amount of oil produced within their boundaries, with the result that the American people are subjected to one of the most blatant forms of price-fixing anywhere in the world. Production is regulated on the state level for two reasons: to prevent companies from pumping oil out of the ground so fast that the pressures in the reservoirs are endangered, thus reducing the amount of oil that can be recovered from the reservoirs; and to keep the prices of crude oil high enough to support a strong market. Both reasons are legitimate, up to a point. Since the states share in the royalties, it is to their advantage to keep the prices reasonably high. But no matter how the golden egg is laid, the taxpayers still pay the maternity bills, in this case every time they drive into a filling station.

In the United States, it is against the law for corporations to engage in price-fixing (i.e., joint production controls that would influence prices). But in the case of the oil companies, it is not necessary. The government does it for them.

However, in recent years it has not been necessary for the states to exercise as much control as they once did. The oil companies know it is to their advantage to practice conservation in terms of removing the oil. And the federal government's rigid import quota system, established during the Eisenhower Administration, automatically set up a seller's market in the United States, reducing the chance of producing too much oil.

There have been documented cases in recent years in which the states restricted production for the sole purpose of raising the price of crude. In December 1970, after the industry announced a price increase of twenty-five cents a barrel, President Nixon attempted to reverse that situation. In Texas and Louisiana, state authorities had imposed controls over production in federal tidelands, and Nixon's advisers felt that the states were deliberately holding down production in an effort to raise prices. On December 4 of that year, Nixon announced that he had directed the Department of the Interior to take over control of the offshore wells from the states. His advisers had predicted that the move could mean a jump in crude oil production by as much as three hundred thousand barrels a day.

Production on state lands remained in the control of the states, however, and they saw to it that the supply did not exceed the demand. The President's Council of Economic Advisers reported that crude oil production in Texas was cut for the month of December by the Railroad Commission upon the suggestion of Mobil Oil Corporation, which had large inventories. The Railroad Commission controls production throughout the rich oil fields of Texas.

The solution to the problem of too much oil was not as neat worldwide, since no government was strong enough to take over price-fixing in the international marketplace. So the industry decided to take care of the problem itself. The result was a worldwide cartel of major oil companies aimed at maintaining a seller's market throughout the entire world. The principals in the scheme were Jersey Standard, Shell, and Anglo-Persian, which accounted for more than 50 percent of the sales outside of the United States. The man behind the plan was Henri Deterding, who at long last was ready to put his ideal of cooperation into effect. Deterding had learned over the years to cut prices with the best of them, but he still believed that in the long run the best solution could only be found in a stable market.

In the summer of 1928, the three majors drafted an agreement aimed at international price-fixing. Basically, the plan prohibited members of the cartel from undermining each other and it attempted to maintain the status quo, allowing the construction of new facilities only when they were absolutely necessary and only when they would not compete with the other members of the cartel.

The setting of prices was particularly interesting. The members of the cartel, which in time included nearly every major producer, agreed to charge a single price for crude oil throughout the world. The amount charged would be the same as the posted price at the American ports along the Gulf of Mexico. Thus if Japan, for instance, wanted to buy oil, it would have to pay the Gulf price.

In addition, companies not included in the cartel were charged for transporting the oil from the Gulf ports, regardless of where the oil actually came from. Thus if a noncartel company in Japan, for example, purchased oil, it was charged for transporting the oil all the way from the Gulf, even if the supply actually came from Indonesia. A few independent firms tried to buck the system, but they were not large enough to meet the demands, and most buyers had to deal with members of the cartel for the bulk of their purchases.

Christopher Tugendhat, in his book, *Oil: The Biggest Business*, cites Sweden as one of the countries where the cartel was especially strong. Quoting from a governmental report issued in 1947, Tugendhat notes that when cartel discussions began in Sweden in 1930, about 97 percent of the market was controlled by six companies, including the Big Three. All six joined a scheme for fixing prices, designating which customers belonged to which companies, and regulating competition. If one of the companies wanted to raise the price for one of his special customers, like the Stockholm tramways, he simply alerted the other members of the cartel and they agreed to quote an even higher price if the customer turned to them.

It is a lot easier to plan these things than put them into effect on a worldwide basis, and the cartel frequently failed. In addition, some governments—most notably France— moved to break up the cartel by aiding the independents and regulating the majors, and in time the cartel weakened. But the cartel had proved one thing to the leaders of the industry. It had demonstrated that they could work together to the advantage of each other, and under-the-counter agreements are commonplace, even today.

Over the years the Middle East fields poured out their riches, fueling fires around the world, and fattening the pocketbooks of the international oil industry. During the late 1940s, when a war-torn world needed more oil than even the Middle East could provide, profits were enormous. Even the oil companies admitted that. Standard Oil of California and Texas, for example, reported net profits of ninety-one cents per barrel in 1948. The companies were still reporting profits of about eighty-five cents a barrel in 1950 when their production was running at over half a million barrels a day.

Such outrageous profits caused grave concern among producing nations. Why should companies—most of which were foreign anyway—realize such gross profits while the nations themselves were forced to settle for much less? At issue was this basic question: Who does the oil belong to? The companies, which have the power and the resources to exploit it? Or the countries, where the oil is a natural resource?

National leaders around the world pondered these questions, but it took a backward little country in Latin America to lead the way. Following the death in 1935 of General Juan Vincente Gomez, the Venezuelan dictator who had given the oil companies everything they wanted in an effort to entice them to exploit his country's rich oil fields, Venezuela erupted in riots that for a while threatened to bathe the country in blood and oil. When order was finally restored by the Army, the nation's leaders were forced to realize that something had to be done if they were to keep their country from entering a state of permanent war.

Under the new dictator, General Eleazar Lopez Contreras, new demands were made of the oil companies, but it was not until the rise to power of General Isaias Medina Angarita that the government took its boldest steps forward. The world was at war, and it was widely known that one of the richest oil fields in the world was in Venezuela. The world thirsted for petroleum, and Medina pushed through a new agreement that gave the government an 80 percent increase in revenue. Medina told his people that a new day had dawned, and he insisted that from that point forward Venezuela would receive an equal share in the profits from her oil. In time it developed that Medina had been wrong; the companies still earned more than the country. The idea of an equal split had caught on in Venezuela, and when the people learned that they were not getting their fair share, they threw their support behind the Opposition Accion Democratica, which mounted a succesful coup against the military government in 1945. On November 12, 1948, an agreement was signed between the oil industry and the new government, which specified that Venzuela would receive 50 percent of the profits. Similar agreements quickly followed in the Middle East, and today every country receives at least half of the profits from the exploitation of its oil. In most cases, this is accomplished through royalties (usually 12½ percent) and taxes.

The new agreement made Venezuela richer than ever, but as is nearly always the case, prosperity did not come cheaply. Nearly seven decades of oil have transformed a onetime sleepy South American country into a nation of continuing transition, complete with all the enormous problems of today.

It has been wisely said that the most revolutionary single event in human history was the development of the small transistor radio. It brought the city to the country, and it made it impossible to disguise the fact that the world of today is a world of contrasts. Young workers in Venezuela's rich farmlands went about their chores with a portable radio pressed against one ear, swinging their way through the fields to the tunes of the city. It did not take long for them to conclude that some people seemed far better off than they, and they left their farms in droves in search of the bright lights and the easy life of the city.

Farms that had once produced fresh fruit and staples to feed the people of Venzuela fell into disuse, with few willing to till the soil. As it turned out, life in the city was not as great as it had sounded. Refugees from the farms built homes out of old flattened tin cans and cardboard on the slopes of the mountains surrounding the city of Caracas, overlooking the magnificent skyscrapers and multilevel freeways built with oil money.

As the 1960s drew to a close, nearly seven hundred thousand Venezuelans, about 10 percent of the country's population, were unemployed or underemployed. Per capita income was listed as one of the highest in Latin America, but even at that it amounted to only $880 a year. Those who turned to the city were lucky if they found jobs as underpaid factory hands. More often, they became street hawkers, trying to bleed out enough money to replace the transistor radio with a television set.

For the farm hand who had fled to the city in search of a better life, only one thing remained certain—some people really were a lot better off, and no explanation for that injustice seemed adequate. Recognizing the seeds of revolution, Venezuela's leaders have tried to make a better life for their people, but transition is rarely easy.

In 1969, Venezuela earned 1.7 billion dollars in foreign exchange. Oil exports accounted for 90 percent of that. But political leaders realized that if Venezuela was to resolve its pressing problems it would need even more money, and the money would most likely have to come from oil. Venezuela's Social-Christian government revealed in 1970 that it would no longer grant concessions to foreign companies. Instead, it would allow them to operate only on a "service contract" basis.

This is the sort of thing that sends chills through the air-conditioned boardrooms of oil companies around the world. There is nothing quite so terrifying to leaders of the oil industry as threats of nationalization of oil operations and, although Venezuela's plans stopped short of that, to oil executives the country had taken a long step in the wrong direction.

There have been repeated attempts in the past by various countries to take over oil interests, but generally the international oil industry has been able to deal with such problems in its own way. Oil is useless if it cannot be marketed, and countries that seize oil properties run the risk of reprisals from all segments of the international industry.

This was demonstrated most recently in Algeria, that north African sanctuary for political expatriots from all over the world. In 1968, Sinclair Mediterranean Petroleum Company accounted for 22,981 barrels a day in oil output from fields in the Algerian desert. In 1969, Sinclair Mediterranean merged with Atlantic Richfield Company, and Algeria promptly declared that Sinclair had forfeited title to its Algerian properties. Algeria said the action was based on the grounds that it had not approved of the merger. The country also announced that it was offering the confiscated properties for competitive bid. In January 1970, the country announced that the "winner" had been Sonatrach, which is owned by the Algerian government.

The thinly veiled seizure was challenged in the International Court of Justice, but the most successful action was taken by Atlantic Richfield in the United States. El Paso Natural Gas Company had planned to purchase up to 1.5 billion cubic feet of liquefied natural gas a day from Sonatrach for import into the United States. Atlantic objected before the Federal Power Commission, and in the fall of 1970, the predictable results came through.

Algeria, which had found that it would not be able to market its oil or gas unless it came to terms with Atlantic Richfield, reached an agreement with the company. The terms of the agreement were not announced, but the president of the company, Robert O. Anderson, stated that the dispute was resolved "in a manner satisfactory to both parties."

Sinclair dropped its suit before the International Court of Justice, and Atlantic Richfield withdrew its objections before the Federal Power Commission. Indeed, the oil industry moves in mysterious ways its wonders to perform.

Such things as the Algerian incident are but minor skirmishes in the history of the oil industry. They have helped establish the industry's distrust of government, and its paranoia over dealing too much with underdeveloped or unstable countries. But of all the elements that have influenced the history of the industry, one stands out above all others as the most significant—war.

War transformed oil from a commercial item into a key element of national defense for every country around the globe. World War I revolutionized the world. The airplane came into its own as an implement of war, and later as the world-shrinking means by which men moved from continent to continent with ease, comfort, and speed. The war led to the development on a large scale of the internal combustion engine as a means of surface transportation. It became necessary to move armies around the world, and that created a need for energy unparalleled in the history of mankind.

At the outset of the war, the United States was producing nearly twice as much oil as the rest of the world combined. The major producing countries in 1913 were the United States, 33 million tons annually; Russia, 8.6 million tons; Mexico, 3.8 million tons; Rumania, 1.9 million tons; Dutch East Indies, 1.6 million tons; Burma and India, 1.1 million tons; and Poland, 1.1 million tons. Germany's lack of oil reveals the country's shortsightedness in terms of energy. Germany could not possibly have won the war without the fuel to feed its machines, and in the end it was just such a shortage that contributed to Germany's defeat.

A quarter of a century later, when war once again loomed on the horizon, both the world and the nature of war had changed, and so had the production of oil. By 1938, the United States still accounted for most of the world's oil production, leading the list with 161.9 million tons a year. A newcomer was next on the list—Venezuela with 27.7 million tons, followed by Iran with 10.2 million tons, Mexico with

5.5 million tons, and Iraq with 4.4 million tons. It is significant that the two American continents accounted for the bulk of the world's oil production.

Germany's leaders recognized that their position in 1938 was not unlike their predicament in 1913. And in that regard they had made a wise decision. Germany limited production of its small domestic oil fields to a minimum, with the intention of using its own oil after the war had begun. A shortage of oil also played a major role in the formation of Germany's battle plans. It was clear to the German commanders in 1938 that one of the reasons they had lost the First World War was their inability to provide enough oil to keep their thirsty machines running. General Erich Ludendorff, commander of the field army of the German Empire from 1916 to 1918, had himself complained that the lack of oil helped bring Germany to her knees. Hitler and his generals decided that if they were to win on the battlefields, victory would have to come swiftly and surely. It was that line of reasoning that gave rise to Germany's *blitzkrieg* strategy, the blistering attacks by the Luftwaffe on pinpointed targets. In the beginning, the strategy worked as planned. Poland and western Europe fell, and Germany seized more oil supplies before turning to Great Britain. England controlled the seas, and Hitler knew that he would have to beat England into submission if he were to bring oil into Germany by tankers.

But England did not fall, and that forced Germany into the long, protracted war that it was least capable of winning. Desperate, Germany turned to the Soviet Union, with the intention of seizing that country's oil fields, but when Hitler's invasion of the Soviet Union failed the fate of the Third Reich was sealed.

On the other side of the world, Japan faced similar problems. Unable to produce enough oil domestically, Japan tried to seize foreign sources to supply its war demands, aiming mainly at the rich fields of Burma and the Dutch East Indies. But in both places the production facilities were largely destroyed before the Japanese took over, and in the end Japan, like Germany, was forced to turn to synthetics as a substitute for oil. Germany managed to convert coal into gasoline, but in time Allied bombing attacks destroyed nearly all of the conversion facilities. Japan was less successful, and in 1945 offered to give some of its few remaining cruisers to the Soviet Union in exchange for oil. The Soviet Union refused.

There were many factors, of course, that led to the defeat of Germany and Japan, but the shortage of oil as a primary source of energy should not be underestimated. Oil means power—and war, after all, is an exercise in power.

It is worth noting that even during the height of World War II the United States managed to import much of its oil, mainly from Venezuela. The program was so successful that most Americans lived nearly as comfortably during wartime as they had during peacetime, buying under some restrictions enough fuel to heat their homes and enough gasoline to run their private chariots. Meanwhile, on the other side of the Atlantic, German troops abandoned their vehicles on the battlefields because they literally ran out of gas.

Much has changed in the years since World War II. Conventional war is still a reality, as evidenced by the prolonged involvement in Vietnam, and the tools of war are even thirstier than they were three decades ago. But the concept of global warfare has changed dramatically, and so has the production of oil.

Rich new fields have been discovered in Mexico and Canada, giving the United States a closer source for imported oil. On the other side of the globe, the Middle East has come into its own with the realization that about 70 percent of the world's proved oil reserves are located there. As of 1970, the United States imported less than 3 percent of its oil from the Middle East, but as the years go by that figure almost certainly will rise. Alhough U.S. companies produce most of the Middle East's oil (100 percent of Saudia Arabia's, 75 percent of Libya's, 50 percent of Kuwait's, 40 percent of Iran's, and 25 percent of Iraq's) there is a distinct chance that the flow of oil from the Middle East could be interrupted from time to time, as it was during the famous Six Day War.

In the past, the countries of the Middle East have pulled against each other rather than together and their lack of co-operation has cost them dearly. But that situation changed dramatically in 1971 when nine major oil-producing countries banded together in a rare display of solidarity.

The nine nations, members of the Organization of Petroleum Exporting Countries (OPEC), were Iran, which led the move, and Algeria, Libya, Kuwait, Saudi Arabia, Abu Dhabi, Qatar, Indonesia and Venezuela. OPEC threatened to cut off oil to the West unless the nations gained a greater share in the profits from their oil.

The nations depend heavily upon the sale of oil for their income, and the threat of cutting off the oil was not regarded as serious by most experts. However, the OPEC succeeded in gaining its basic goals, although details of the settlements between the industry and the countries have been shrouded in secrecy. The cost will be passed on to the consumers.

The significance of the 1971 confrontation lies in the unity among the nations of OPEC. A new day has dawned among the smaller producing nations. It all adds up to a less comfortable position for nations which have to import much of their oil, and in the years ahead that group will include the United States, unless alternatives to oil can be developed. And no experts seriously believe that there is enough oil beneath the continental shelf to change that picture significantly.

From a national security standpoint, the ideal situation for any country is to be self-sufficient when it comes to oil. But because of America's tremendous demands, the United States will never again be able to produce all the oil it needs. And as the years pass, the percentage of imported oil will increase. By 1980, America is expected to import at least half of its oil.

What does that mean in terms on national security? Probably very little. Conventional war is likely to be isolated, as in the case of Vietnam, and isolated wars are not capable of cutting off the flow of oil from ports on the other side of the world. On the other hand, a global conflict is not likely to be of the nature of World War II. In this age of thermonuclear capability, global warfare is likely to be swift and sure, and the chances of a long, drawn-out world war seem remote. Even if that unlikelihood were to come to pass, the United States almost surely would be allied with other producing nations, such as Canada and Mexico, and some oil could be imported, just as it was at the height of World War II.

But given all those factors, it would seem that conservation of the nation's oil reserves is at least as important as exploitation. Ironically, the oil industry argued that same line back in the 1950s when the major corporations were fighting the trend toward the imposition of import controls. In 1958, just before President Eisenhower moved to restrict the imports, the Petroleum Industry Research Foundation issued a staff paper titled "United States Oil Imports, A Case Study in International Trade."

"Virtually all of the oil imported into the United States is produced by American oil companies from concessions they possess in foreign countries," the paper argued. "The petroleum import trade cannot be subjected to discrimination by foreign suppliers."

The paper went on to assert that "The risk that the United States might be cut off from all its foreign oil sources for reasons other than a major military conflict is virtually nonexistent. The worldwide and growing dispersion of America's foreign oil sources and the considerable spare producing capacity of each of them prevents this."

"Measured against the various clear and significant advantages, the risks of supplementary oil imports to national security are limited and remote. The bulk of America's foreign oil comes from nearby Western Hemisphere countries. Most of these are actually in a better geographic position than domestic producing regions to supply America's major oil consuming areas. Therefore, foreign oil shipping routes to these areas are unlikely to be more endangered than domestic ones by future military actions," the paper concluded.

That is the way the domestic oil industry looked at the problem of national security back in the 1950s, when it was fighting attempts by the federal government to impose restrictions on imports. Since that time, the restrictions have been leveled, the price of domestic crude oil has gone up, and it is now to the industry's advantage to keep the restrictions in effect.

It is not surprising that nowadays, whenever anyone suggests removing the import controls, representatives of the oil industry immediately denounce the suggestion as a threat to the national security.

In his annual report delivered in 1968, Union Oil Company's president Fred Hartley even went so far as to suggest that attempts by the government to weaken the oil import quota system were "immoral." Hartley told his stockholders:

"Your company feels, too, that it has a responsibility to speak out on issues that concern not only our operations but conceivably also the safety of our country as well. I have particular reference to the Oil Import Program, which was originally designed to retain a strong domestic oil industry to provide for our national security. Under the unfair and immoral administration of the Department of Interior, however, the Oil Import Program has been distorted and confused to accommodate the special interests and special privileges of alleged anti-poverty programs, air pollution control, small business, World War II allies, chemical companies, certain refiners and marketers."

Amid the shouting and the screaming about national security, several facts should be kept in mind. First, oil is important for national security. Second, it is readily available in wide areas of the world. Third, importation of some oil is unavoidable. Fourth, the United States has enormous reserves within its continental limits, and during a time of war, production from these reserves could be increased tremendously. And fifth, the wailing and gnashing of teeth by leaders of the oil industry contributes little toward understanding the problem, particularly in view of the fact that the industry's position has shifted in keeping with its profits.

The American people are continually subjected to propaganda campaigns from the oil industry. Most elected leaders remember World War II, and many of the arguments ring true. But the world has changed since 1945, and it will change even more in the years ahead. The demand today is for reason, not reaction.

The role of the international oil industry in today's society is not easily understood. Reasonable men and women find it hard to believe that an industry would deliberately use such issues as national security to argue for its own profiteering.

It is impossible to separate the oil industry of today from its past. It is true that hundreds of smaller companies have robbed the majors of much of their control over the industry, but oil interests exert more influence over the American way of life than most people realize.

The industry has changed some since John D. Rockfeller held the nation in his grip. Today, air-conditioned boardrooms are the style, and distinguished men in neatly tailored suits preside over what has become the world's biggest and most powerful business. Like Rockefeller, the new leaders create their conglomerates by swallowing the little people who try to infringe upon their territory, and they build vast empires that span continents and encircle the globe. And like Rockefeller, they win friends by contributing millions to popular charities, and then turn around and raise their prices at the gas pump.

The industry is what it is today largely because of its past. Its game is to make money. Its tool is power. It has an abundance of each, and it uses both freely.

8

The oil industry has long recognized that power is the first element of survival. And as the industry matured in the United States, it made sure that men who saw the world as they saw it were elected to high public office. Once they were in office, the "public servants" guaranteed that the needs of the industry were served.

In recent years, five powerful men have stood out for their patronage of the oil industry. But of the five, only one remains in power today—Russell Long. Of the other four, three are dead and the fourth—former President Lyndon B. Johnson—has retired to his ranch in Texas.

For many years Johnson wielded great power as Senate majority leader, a position that gave him the means to see to it that no foes of the industry found their way onto the Senate Finance Committee. The late Senate minority leader, Everett McKinley Dirksen, shared Johnson's views and admitted that he held a profound and undisguised commitment to the industry's welfare, according to the New York *Times* Magazine (March 8, 1970).

As leaders of their respective parties in the upper house, Johnson and Dirksen controlled the committees that controlled the Senate, giving the oil industry a bastion within the hallowed walls of the United States Senate.

Even with their combined power, it is doubtful that Senators Johnson and Dirksen rivaled the authority of that legendary Texan, Sam Rayburn, longtime Speaker of the House and for many years one of the most powerful men on

Capitol Hill. As Speaker, Rayburn referred bills to committees, and by a single whisk of his pen condemned unfavorable
legislation by sending it to an unfavorable committee. He
also was in a position to exercise great power in the House
Rules Committee and the House Ways and Means Committee, which controlled the levying of taxes. Until his death
in 1961, Rayburn reigned over Washington like no other
congressional leader in modern history, and if a single man
had the power to control the U. S. Congress, it was Sam
Rayburn.

Russell Long's predecessor as chairman of the Senate Finance Committee was the late Senator Robert Kerr of Okla-
homa. Kerr was a zealous guardian of the industry, partly
because of his interest in Kerr-McGee Oil Industries, Inc.
For many years Kerr saw to it that legislation that would
damage his business was killed in his Senate Finance Committee, and following his death in 1963 the cloak passed
to his carefully schooled mentor, Russell Long, also an oil
man.

Johnson and Rayburn, who hailed from a state that depends heavily upon the oil industry, controlled both houses
of the U. S. Congress simultaneously for many years. In
1964, when Johnson ran for his first full term as President,
the oil industry supported a Democratic presidential hopeful
for the first time in recent history.

With powerful allies such as these, it is little wonder that
the oil industry has enjoyed benefits and tax breaks that
stagger the imagination. It is no surprise that such tax loopholes as the oil depletion allowance stood intact for more
than four decades. It was reduced in 1969 from 27.5 percent to 22 percent, and it is no accident that the first reduction in the allowance came after four of the five greatest
champions of the industry had passed from the scene. Although he tried, Russell Long was not enough to carry the
fight alone.

There is still little doubt that the oil industry wields more
power in Washington than any other special-interest group,

but it remains to be seen whether the American people will be able to keep the U. S. Congress from passing back into the hands of the oil industry to the degree that it once was.

None of this should surprise anyone who is familiar with the history of the industry. Oil companies have always sought to control the politicians who are supposed to control them. What is surprising is that the industry dropped the ball and let some of the power shift into hands that are not entirely sympathetic to the oil industry.

A number of men have risen to power in recent years and have challenged the industry on several fronts, such as Wisconsin's courageous William Proxmire. One of the most interesting cases involves Tennessee's former Senator Albert Gore. Gore, a liberal Democrat who was defeated in his bid for re-election in 1970, saw something few of his contemporaries had noticed, and he blew the whistle on the oil industry. After the election, Gore speculated privately that oil money had contributed to his defeat, but he conceded that he probably lost the election because of his liberal stance on such issues as civil rights.

What had Gore seen?

He had seen simply that the oil industry was up to its old tricks. One of the reasons the industry has been successful over the years is that it has managed to adjust itself to meet changing demands. When it found, for example, that it had too much oil on its hands, it stimulated new markets and found new uses for petroleum, and in time the problem was solved. In recent years, however, leaders in the industry have realized that the nation's energy needs are changing; for the first time in history those needs cannot be met entirely by more oil. The need in the years ahead will not only be for more energy, but for different energy. In many areas, electrical power is expected to eliminate some of the needs for crude oil—the home of the future may be heated entirely by electricity, for example—and the petroleum industry in the 1960s decided that it would have to get with the times.

One indication of this came in the late 1960s, when Gulf Oil Company purchased General Atomic in San Diego from General Dynamics. At that time, General Atomic was advertised as the largest privately owned nuclear research center in the world. For the first time the oil industry had made major inroads into the field of nuclear energy.

Gore got into the act when the Tennessee Valley Authority announced a 23 percent jump in electric rates for its customers. Gore asked why, and he was told that the price of coal had risen 56 percent during the first half of 1970. And the Authority was having trouble buying enough coal even at that price. Normally, the TVA tried to keep enough coal on hand to last at least three or four weeks, just in case the supply was interrupted. But by the fall of 1970, the TVA was down to a few days' supply, and other electrical power plants indicated similar problems.

Gore investigated, and he learned that a number of major coal companies had been purchased by oil firms. The writing was on the wall. The industry had turned the calendar back a hundred years and, as in the days of John D. Rockefeller, the oil industry was trying once again to establish a monopoly, this time by seizing control of all sources of energy.

Deeply troubled, on September 10, 1970, Gore appeared before the Senate's Subcommittee on Materials, Mining, and Fuels. Because of its importance, most of his talk is quoted here:

The shortage of coal is of particular concern to me. I represent, in part, a state which is a coal producer, and a coal consumer. We still mine a good deal of coal in Tennessee. In 1969, production amounted to more than eight million tons. But we consume a lot of coal in Tennessee. At the moment, I am concerned about the coal supply for TVA, one of the largest users in the world. TVA consumed about thirty-one million tons of coal in fiscal year 1970 in its entire system.

The people of Tennessee, and of the entire Tennessee River Valley, are perhaps more vulnerable to a shortage of coal, and electricity, as well as to large variations in price, than are the people of some other sections of the country. TVA has done a good job of selling electricity, and the whole idea of electrification, in its area. Many homes are heated by electricity, and many industries, having come into the valley after the advent of TVA, are absolutely dependent on large amounts of electricity at reasonable rates.

So, Mr. Chairman, although many parts of the country are hard hit by the current shortage—artifically induced, in my opinion—of coal and other fuels, the effects of this shortage are apt to be more severe in Tennessee than in many other parts of the country, though the problem looms nationally.

Of course, action of the most significance in the short run can be taken only by the President. He could take action now on a number of fronts, should he so desire. He could begin antitrust action in order to restore some semblance of competition. He could put short supply export controls on coal. He could use the moral force and power of his office to bring some of the big oil companies into line. And it is the oil companies and their influence which constitute the major problem.

Indeed, if one looks at the list of suppliers of TVA's coal last year, and notes the coal companies which are owned or controlled by noncoal operators, both the cause of the problem and its cure become readily apparent. More than 60 percent of TVA's coal last year came from companies owned by noncoal producers. The oil company owners included two giants—Standard of Ohio, and Gulf. Among non-oil company owners of TVA's coal suppliers were such conglomerates as General Dynamics and American Metal Climax.

So long as this concentration of coal properties in the hands of oil and other conglomerates continues—and this situation began to develop in fairly recent years—we will have price fixing and artificially induced shortages in the supply of coal.

A few days ago I had a telegram from Mr. Donald Cook, President of the American Electric Power Company. Mr. Cook placed a major part of the blame for the current crisis in coal on exports. This is certainly a large part of the short-run problem. Exports are now running at a sharply increased rate and now amount to about 10 percent of total domestic production.

But this is the easiest part of the over-all problem to deal with. The President could take care of this with a stroke of the pen. I have asked him to do so. No legislation is required for President Nixon to put export controls on coal. A few years ago, when we had a Secretary of Commerce from North Carolina, and furniture manufacturers in North Carolina got upset about a sudden rise in the price of walnut logs, then being exported in quantity, it did not require much time for controls to be placed on the exportation of walnut logs. The coal crisis is much more in evidence and much more damaging to the whole economy and national health.

Coal stocks at many of TVA's generating plants, as well as plants of many utilities around the country, both privately and publicly owned, stand at dangerously low levels. A national crisis in energy impends.

On August 27 there was only enough coal on hand at two of TVA's plants, Colbert and John Sevier, to run at full capacity for four days. At the Johnsonville and Kingston plants there was a five-day supply of coal. Widows Creek had six days of coal on hand. Other TVA plants were somewhat better off. Over-all, TVA had on hand last week about one-fifth the supply of coal it considers appropriate, necessary, and prudent to insure uninterrupted service.

The slightest interruption in day-to-day deliveries would necessitate shutting down several generating plants. And this would, in turn, mean not only discomfort and inconvenience for millions of homeowners, but also the loss of jobs for thousands of employees in industries and commercial establishments that cannot operate without electricity.

This sorry situation did not develop overnight. It has been in the making for several years, even though it has become apparent to the general public with disconcerting suddenness. And it has come about not by chance, but through the careful planning of some of our major corporations, and with the knowledge and tacit approval, if not the open support, of the Nixon Administration through tax favoritism and inaction on both export control on coal and permission for increased imports of fuel oil.

The need for maintaining a steady growth in the supply of cheap electricity is so obvious as not to require elaboration. . . .

The remarkable economic growth we have enjoyed since World War II is closely related to the expansion of facilities and capacity for generation of electric power. At present rates of growth, electric generating capacity must double every ten years. But at this moment, we are simply not prepared to keep up. . . .

The key fuel, insofar as electric power generation is concerned, is coal. Excluding hydropower, coal accounts for 63 percent of fuel used by our electric utilities. This may be reduced as time goes on as more nuclear generating capacity is brought into operation, but at the present time and for several years to come we must continue to depend on coal to a great extent. And the coal companies, until quite recently, have met the challenge of production. Generating plants use four times more coal now than they did at the end of World War II, and the independent coal companies have heretofore increased output through advances in mining techniques and mechanization. One man now produces almost twenty tons of coal per day, compared to 5.8 tons at the end of World War II.

Our other sources of energy—oil, natural gas, hydropower, and nuclear energy—are also important, but they, too, are either in short supply or with limited production.

Production of domestic oil is regulated by the various States.

A rather tight lid is kept on production in order to insure a good price. And, while foreign oil importation could relieve the production and price problem, a tight import quota system remains in effect.

Natural gas is in short supply—at least where it is needed. While producers complain that government regulations inhibit sufficient gas production and exploration, there are reports that gas is being artificially held back from would-be consumers.

Coal production is more than ten million tons short of probable consumption this year. And the coal companies no longer independently controlled, show no signs of wanting production to catch up with consumption.

Nuclear power has not come on as fast as had been predicted. Over-all, the program is two or three years behind. Of the sixty-five nuclear power plants scheduled for service between 1970 and 1976, twenty-three have already been delayed by up to a year.

Hydropower seems about to have nearly reached its limits. New sites are extremely scarce. Some progress may be made in pump-storage procedures to allow some extra generation during peak load hours, but this appears to be all that can be done in this direction now.

To sum up, we must depend on oil, gas, coal, and nuclear energy to meet increased electricity demand. And the frightening thing about all of this is that we now have a quasi-monopoly in these fuels. The big oil companies are making a determined effort to attain control of all energy sources. In fact, they already, with help from the Nixon Administration, manage effective control of both coal and oil.

During the past five years, the oil companies have been busily buying up the larger coal producers. They have also been busy in the nuclear area, and may soon even be in a position to dominate absolutely the production of nuclear fuels.

Already, the squeeze on the consumer is tight. Coal prices are being raised at the rate of 56 percent per year; fuel oil is up about 48 percent. Already, the additional cost to the consumer from these fuel price increases amounts to a billion dollars per year through higher electric bills. . . .

Several reasons have been advanced for our sudden shortage of coal. It has been suggested that there is a shortage of freight cars, and there is a shortage. It is felt by some that the Federal Coal Mine Health and Safety Act of 1969 has been responsible for closing some mines and increasing cost of coal. Some smaller mines are closed, although there has been a spurt in strip mining. There has been an increase in exportation of coal, and this has been felt both in the supply and in the price. Some feel there is a shortage of manpower for mining.

But I submit that an overriding reason for coal shortages and increased prices lies in the concentration of ownership of our nation's coal supplies and producers in a few giant corporations which also own oil and gas operations, and in the reluctance or refusal of President Nixon to exercise the powers available to him either to limit the export of coal or to permit an increase in the importation of fuel oil. . . .

Rather, through continuation of the oil import quota program, through the recent and thoroughly unjustified hike in the cost of nuclear fuel enrichment, through failure to enforce the antitrust laws, through resistance to true tax reform, and by creating a climate conducive to further big business grabs, much is being done actually to destroy competitive, free enterprise.

Beginning in 1965, the independent coal companies began to disappear. This disappearance was not brought about through failure to make a profit or inability to continue in business. The disappearance was, rather, brought about by consolidations and acquisitions. And, most disturbing to me was the fact that many of the largest coal companies were being bought up by oil companies. I warned Congress and the people of my state about this threat of monopoly in 1966. Moreover, I tried to strike down the tax favoritism that spanned the fuel monopoly. In 1966, I warned senators: "I can foresee a situation, not far off, when we will no longer have an independent coal industry. We may well have all major energy sources—petroleum, coal, uranium—under the control of a very few powerful corporations."

Perhaps I am overly sensitive to the depredations of big oil companies, though I do not think so. I have fought them consistently since I have been in Congress, and, in turn, they have fought me and continue to do so. Now the public feels their deep bite.

The alarming fact we now face is the ownership of a large part of our coal reserves by oil companies, and other giant conglomerates not primarily concerned with coal production. Eight of our ten largest coal companies are owned by oil or mineral corporations. And according to TVA power manager James Watson, the oil companies are not particularly concerned about selling coal.

Coal companies, under their new ownership and new management policies, simply refuse to bid when asked to do so. A recent experience by TVA had been duplicated, I understand, in other parts of the country. TVA asked for bids for delivery of 140,000 tons of coal per week for one of its new steam plants. It received only one bid, and that for only twenty thousand tons. And the price was very high.

TVA has announced a whopping 23 percent increase. This is a sharp blow to homeowners and industries in the Tennessee Valley.

An electric utility, public or private, must meet its increased costs sooner or later. And these increases, brought about largely through increased cost of fuel and through higher interest rates, must be paid by the consumer.

In the case of TVA, the 23 percent increase in rates will cost 115 million dollars per year. This is a heavy burden on the people of Tennessee and the valley.

But suppose TVA tries to switch to oil or gas. It must largely deal with the same capital interests.

In the last few years, many of our major oil companies have acquired holdings in competing fuels. Of course, they have always had a tight grasp on gas. They made a real breakthrough in coal in 1966 when Continental Oil took over Consolidation Coal—a deal I unsuccessfully fought. The pace of acquisition quickened after that and today, as I have said, eight of the ten largest coal producers are owned by oil, mineral, or other industrial giants. . . .

Now, with the oil companies controlling most of the fossil fuels, the only remaining hope for competition rests with nuclear fuel. And whose tracks do we find in the nuclear field?

According to testimony presented to the Senate Antitrust Subcommittee, oil companies now control 45 percent of known uranium reserves. Oil companies control uranium milling. Oil companies own four out of five plants for reprocessing used nuclear fuel elements.

About the only operation in the nuclear field not already dominated by oil companies is the enrichment process, which the Federal Government now controls. President Nixon, true to form, has been busying himself to find a way to "sell" these enrichment plants at Oak Ridge, Paducah, and Portsmouth to private enterprise. I have spoken out on this matter many times, as have other members of the Senate, particularly those who are on the Joint Committee on Atomic Energy. I will not repeat what I have already said. I will say at this point only that I will continue to oppose to the utmost of my ability the President's planned giveaway of the people's assets in the nuclear processing plants.

The Nixon Administration recently announced a 10 percent rise in the cost of enriching nuclear fuel. This was wholly unnecessary, and can serve only to underpin the oil companies' price increases on fossil fuels, as well as to prepare the way further for a profitable commercial operation of nuclear fuel enrichment when the contemplated giveaway of the enrichment plants finally surfaces in full bloom. . . .

The time for action has arrived. Consumers must not be burdened with what amounts to a transfer of taxes from the oil companies to them. Utilities such as TVA must be allowed to operate in a more truly competitive situation in the purchase of fuel.

The Nixon Administration talks a great game of "free enterprise." I now call on President Nixon to help preserve free enterprise by restoring competition to the fuel field. How can he continue to ignore this shaky situation in fuels brought on by oil company concentration?

Export controls should be placed on coal. I would not deny any exports at all, but they should be held down to the level of recent years before the big jump in 1968–69. Our own needs come first. That is why we have the Export Control Act.

Next, antitrust action is obviously the first step to be taken. The hold of the oil companies on our fuel supply must be broken. The giant conglomerates involving coal producers must be broken up and at once. I call upon the Administration for this needed action.

Third, tax changes which would discourage conglomerates should be adopted. This would require congressional action, which I urge.

Fourth, the import quota program on oil should be discontinued. The President extended this import quota only a few weeks ago. I call upon the President to rescind this in the public interest.

I am concerned, seriously concerned, over the concentrated control which now exists in fuels. This is most dangerous to the national welfare, both in the short run and in the long run. It must not be tolerated. Government, as the agent for the whole society, must act for the common good. This is the purpose of government. Why else should we tolerate such an expensive, wasteful, irritating thing as our national government? We tolerate its shortcomings in the expectation that it will, on occasion, move to our defense. This is such an occasion.

Unless something is done now, the oil industry will be even more powerful in the years ahead. The federal government has indicated that 60 percent of the nation's electricity will be generated by nuclear power plants within the next thirty years. Standard Oil of New Jersey, which is already the world's largest oil company, is on its way to becoming the uranium leader as well. Jersey Standard, which also owns a huge share of the nation's coal mines, revealed plans in 1970 to open two large uranium mines. Other leaders in the uranium field are the late Senator Robert Kerr's firm, Kerr-McGee Oil Industries, Inc., and Gulf Oil Company and Atlantic Richfield Company.

It would appear that the oil industry has come full circle. According to a report by the National Economic Research Association, Inc., which was submitted to the Senate Antitrust Committee in 1970, the industry, indeed, is up to its old tricks. The report, called "Competition in the Energy Markets," warned that the expansion of the petroleum industry is "comparable to the formation of the trusts in the latter decade of the nineteenth century. In short, the oil companies, themselves portraying their activities as efforts at diversification, are in fact systematically acquiring their competition."

Why doesn't somebody do something?

A man by the name of Albert Gore tried, but a funny thing happened on the way to the ballot box.

9

The age of oil did not begin with Drake's Well. Nor did it begin with the rise to power of John D. Rockefeller. The age of oil dawned when Henry Ford started cranking out his Tin Lizzies toward the end of the past century. True, that event also spawned the age of the automobile, but in a real sense the two were the same. Henry Ford gave the common man the vehicle to broaden his world beyond his wildest imagination; but without an abundant supply of fuel to power the Lizzie, Ford's creation would have been nothing other than an expensive toy for the idle rich.

Ford's creation revolutionized the world, but it was a revolution fueled by petroleum. Within the past century, man has moved from the country to the cities; he has molded his lifestyle around the theme of industrial progress; he has beat his ploughshare into a power lawnmower. The key to all of this has been energy—electricity to run his power tools, gasoline to run his cars, natural gas to heat his factories. Oil and its frequent companion, natural gas, have supplied the major share of the energy to meet these demands. But in recent years oil has taken on a new dimension, and its role in contemporary society is enormous.

Many years ago, scientists discovered that oil derivatives could be used in many ways. The result has been the remarkable growth of the petrochemical industry—the Midas touch that transformed black crude oil into miracle fabrics, detergents, explosives, insecticides, fertilizers, plastics, *ad in-*

finitum. . . . Indeed, oil is so valuable that it seems almost criminal to burn it.

Yet burn it we do, in ever-increasing quantities, for ever-increasing reasons. And burn it we shall for many years to come. For in spite of the many uses of oil, its most valuable role is still its potential for being transformed into energy.

Thus it is that oil has been a cursed blessing for man. In many ways it has enriched his life, but enrichment has not come cheaply. There is ample evidence that in the years ahead that pattern will intensify. Scientists believe we have just begun to scrape the surface in the field of petrochemicals, and some day we may indeed ride about in plastic capsules that can be recycled when no longer usable. But the thirst for oil and all forms of energy has placed man on a collision course with nature.

The demand for energy seems insatiable. But every attempt to meet that demand has serious faults. The question now is not how do we meet the demand without creating serious problems. The question, instead, is how do we meet the demand and create the fewest serious problems. There is no neat solution.

Today's industrial society is like a good man who is hooked on a bad woman. No matter how many times he tells himself she is no good, he keeps going back for more. In the same sense, as long as we insist on "progress," we are going to be cursed with its by-products.

The great threat in the years ahead is that man will yield to the simplest solutions, although they may not be the best. No one would deny that the need for energy will be profound. It will be so great, in fact, that there will be a strong temptation to exploit every source, regardless of the consequences.

The oil industry is fond of pointing out that oil reserves are limited, and it is therefore necessary to proceed on all fronts. But other natural resources are also limited, such as the seashores, and when a collision is inevitable the nation must decide how to avoid making an irreversible error. It sounds reasonably simple. But the resolution of the present crisis will be anything but simple.

Any solution necessarily involves two major factors: the demand for energy in the years ahead, and the availability of fuels to meet that need. It is old law of supply and demand, cluttered with international complications, political intrigue, legitimate uncertainties, and deliberate smokescreens.

What will be this nation's energy demands in the future? Even the best experts disagree widely, because the future is cloudy, even for experts. Who would have predicted, for example, that the Vietnam war would become this nation's longest war?

Where will we get the fuel to supply our needs? Again, the experts differ widely. No one knows, for instance, exactly how much oil lies beneath the North American continent.

Scores of publications seeking to answer these questions are distributed each year. Most are produced by industries that have something to gain—such as the oil industry—and the figures frequently reflect the world as they would have us see it. Publications by the petroleum industry make it sound as though the nation is facing an immediate energy crisis. This simply is not the case.

One of the most comprehensive reports on the nation's supply and demand for energy was released in the fall of 1970. The report, titled "The Economy, Energy, and the Environment," was prepared for the Joint Economic Committee of the U. S. Congress by the environmental policy division of the Library of Congress. That report, incidentally, recommended a "go slow" policy in the development of offshore oil fields. Most of the figures in this chapter were taken from that report. The figures are staggering, and hard to relate to daily human experiences, but they give solid indication of the fantastic scope of the energy problem.

In the report's opening comments, the role of energy in modern life was illustrated like this:

"A full-grown man is capable of an average power output of about 1/20th of a horsepower during an eight-hour working day, equivalent to an output of about thirty-seven watts of electrical energy. Thus, when a child turns on a 150-watt television receiver, he commands electrical energy equivalent to the energy output of four grown men. As long as human progress depended mostly on the energy of human muscles, there could not be much physical change in the conditions of primitive life."

The report goes on to state that those who have supplied the fuels for energy have managed to stay well ahead of the demand in the past and almost certainly will do so in the future. As the report put it:

The growth in use of energy in the United States is dynamic and is outpacing the growth in population. If the past is any indication of the future, new energy sources will crowd into the energy marketplace before existing sources are depleted. During the 1860s about 75 percent of the nation's inanimate energy supply came from wood. By 1900, wood supplied only 21 percent of the energy, with coal dominant with 71 percent of the energy market. By the later 1930s, oil and gas were challenging the position of coal and shortly after World War II were supplying more energy than coal.

The years following World War II saw another shift as the use of natural gas grew faster than crude oil. In 1968, natural gas production, including liquids made from natural gas, supplied 34.7 percent of the nation's energy. Domestic crude oil supplied 35.3 percent; including oil imports raises the oil's share to 40.1 percent. The higher rate of gas consumption combined with increase demands for protection of the quality of the environment, logically could result in natural gas becoming the nation's largest energy source within a few years if adequate supplies are available. However, there is present doubt about the adequacy of natural gas supply.

As for present use of energy, according to a recent report of the Bureau of Mines, the energy consumption of the United States in 1969 was the highest ever.

Energy equivalent to 65,645 trillion British Thermal Units

was required to meet the nation's total 1969 requirements for heat, light, and all forms of power. This represents a 5.1 percent increase over 1968 consumption, slightly below the previous year's growth rate.

The record energy demand was met principally through increased use of natural gas and petroleum, plus slight increases in the use of coal, hydropower, and nuclear power.

Compared with ten years ago, 1969 energy consumption represents a 51.2 percent increase at an average of 4.2 percent annually over the past decade. Over that ten-year period, the Bureau noted, consumption of dry natural gas grew 75.4 percent; water power, 55.8 percent; petroleum and natural gas liquids, 44.4 percent; and bituminous coal and lignite, 37.7 percent. Anthracite consumption declined 49.8 percent. Nuclear energy, whose use in generating electric power was negligible ten years ago, jumped to 141 trillion Btu.

In terms of consumption, the largest energy increase of 1969 was in electric utility power (12.1 percent), followed by energy for household and commercial needs (6.9 percent), industrial uses (5.2 percent), and transportation (4 percent).

Petroleum, continuing as the dominant fuel, supplied 43.2 percent of all U.S. energy demands in 1969. The other energy sources, and each one's share in meeting the year's total energy needs, were natural gas (excluding natural gas liquids), 32.1 percent; bituminous coal and lignite, 20.1 percent; waterpower, 4 percent; anthracite, 0.4 percent; and nuclear energy, 0.2 percent.

As for the future, the report states:

Although nuclear power supplies only a minute part of present energy demands, some forecasters expect uranium and thorium will become the largest single source of energy for the nation within the next three decades. However, given our larger resources of coal and oil shale, and the technological prospects for converting them into fluid fuels, the dominance of the petroleum like fuels is thought likely to continue for the rest of this century. For the more distant future, there are hopes that certain forms of hydrogen atoms, which are present in nature, can be used as fuel in the fusion process, which in essence could provide an inexhaustible supply.

. . . the Office of Science and Technology recently released the results of a study made for it by the Battelle Memorial Institute which compared many recent forecasts of energy supply and demand. According to this report, energy consumption in the year 2000, including nonfuel uses, is expected to be about 170,000 trillion British Thermal Units if real gross national product grows at about 4 percent per year. Consumption in 1968 was slightly over 62,000 Btu. The average annual indicated growth rate is about 3.2 percent.

Although a figure of 170,000 trillion Btu in the year 2000 appears reasonable to the Institute, on the basis of extrapolating current trends, it does not reflect the effect of new factors which are already emerging. Most important of these is the growing concern for protecting the environment. Also this figure may not adequately reflect possible changes in efficiency of energy conversion and changes in the pattern of energy use, especially the larger share expected to go into electric power production.

All of the existing projections analyzed by the Institute estimate that oil (including natural gas liquids) will continue to be the nation's largest source of energy through the year 2000. Natural gas, excluding liquid fuels made from natural gas, is expected to continue to be the second largest source of energy. Of three projections for both nuclear power and coal at the end of the century, one estimates that coal will provide slightly more energy than nuclear, another estimates just the opposite, and one foresees a large margin for nuclear. At the moment the Federal Power Commission and the Atomic Energy Commission favor the second estimate.

Hydroelectric power is expected to continue to grow but to be of decreasing relative importance and to supply the smallest amount of any of the commercial energy sources in the year 2000. Nuclear generation is expected to exceed hydro-electric generation sometime between the years 1975-80.

A consistent rate of growth of energy consumption toward the expected figure of 170,000 trillion Btu for the year 2000 would require 3.4 quintillion (3.4×10^{18}) Btu in the 32 years from 1968 to 2000. This is equivalent to the energy in 590 billion barrels of crude oil or 170 billion tons of average grade U.S. coal resources, assuming 20 million Btu per ton.

Relative to past consumption, expected consumption in the 32 years 1968 to 2000 will be almost three (2.8) times that at the prior 32 years, 1936 to 1968. Providing fuel to generate such quantities of energy will pose a substantial problem for the energy industries and for government policy, since the nation has been consuming its higher grade, more accessible resources first and since even the much smaller energy consumption of the last three decades has already created serious environmental problems.

To a large degree, the nature of the energy will be determined by the area of the nation in which it is used. Electricity, for example, will continue to be produced from coal in areas where there is an abundance of coal, by fuel oil residues where oil is abundant, by hydroelectric power in areas that are fortunate enough to have hydroelectric facilities, and by nuclear reactors in other areas. Nuclear power is expected to compete with other fuels in the New England states, in the Middle Atlantic states except for coal-rich Pennsylvania, throughout most South Atlantic states except for West Virginia, in parts of the East Central states, and in all of the Pacific Coast states.

One of the basic problems in nuclear power is that while most people like the idea of "harnessing the atom for peaceful purposes," nobody seems to want to live next door to a nuclear reactor. Attempts to build nuclear power plants have been thwarted in various areas of the country and there is reason to believe that the fight will go on.

The Federal Atomic Energy Commission (AEC) claims

there is little chance of a major accident from a nuclear reactor. However, a report issued by the AEC in 1957—which the AEC has not since revised—gives cause for careful thought. The report outlined the possible consequences of such an accident. It stated:

"The theoretical estimates indicate that personal damage might range from a lower limit of none injured or killed to an upper limit, in the worst case, of about thirty-four hundred killed and about forty-five thousand injured.

"Theoretical property damages ranged from a lower limit of about one-half million dollars to an upper limit in the worst case of about seven billion dollars. This latter figure is largely due to assumed contamination of land with fission products.

"Under adverse combinations of conditions considered, it was estimated that people could be killed at distances up to fifteen miles and injured at distances of about forty-five miles. Land contamination could extend for greater distances.

"In the large majority of theoretical reactor accidents considered, the total assumed losses would not exceed a few hundred million dollars."

However, at least one prominent American has no serious objections to living near a nuclear reactor. President Richard M. Nixon purchased a summer home in the Southern California community of San Clemente in 1969. One of the President's industrial neighbors is the large pioneer nuclear generating plant at San Onofre, just south of San Clemente.

Statistics indicate that petroleum will play the dominant role in the nation's energy needs of the near future. In 1968 oil was the basic energy source for only about 7.8 percent of the nation's electricity. However, it continues to be the main source of energy for such things as transportation. Such a profound demand on a worldwide basis justifies the basic question: Can we find enough oil? The Library of Congress report tried to answer that question this way:

According to recently published research, free world petroleum explorers have uncovered more than half (59 percent) of all existing giant fields since 1950. Of the known seventy-one giant fields, defined as those good for at least one billion barrels of ultimate recoverable reserves (past production plus remaining reserves) twenty-one were discovered in the 1950s and at least another twenty-one have been found during the 1960s. Those seventy-one fields originally held about 360 billion barrels of such reserves; of that amount some 62.5 billion barrels have already been produced, leaving an estimated 297 billion barrels of recoverable reserves, or about 74 percent of the free world reserve.

Of the seventy-one fields, thirty-eight are in the Middle East and only eighteen in the Western Hemisphere, of which eleven are in North America. There are, of course, a good many known smaller fields, particularly in the United States. For example, if the cutoff size were set at an estimated ultimate recovery of 100 million barrels or more per field, the United States alone has 259 oil and forty-seven gas giants, which are indicated as now producing about 51 percent of the national output and holding 57 percent of the remaining reserve.

But for the free world, the six largest fields are indicated to contain more than 47 percent of total recoverable oil, and none of those six is in North America; five are in the Middle East and one in Venezuela. Not only are few of the North American entries anywhere near the top in size but for the most part they were discovered rather early and have been rather intensively developed. For example, of the U.S. monsters, East Texas, Wilminton, Yates, Kelly-Snyder, Midway-Sunset, and Huntington Beach were all discovered before 1950, one of them as early as 1901, and have yielded about half or more of their ultimate recoverable oil. Elk Hills (Naval oil reserve) is an exception; though discovered in 1920, the great bulk of its reserve is still in the ground. That also is the case of the two monster Canadian fields, Pembina, discovered in 1953, and Swan Hills, 1957.

The discovery in 1968 on Alaska's North Slope (Prudhoe Bay) is not included in the list of seventy-one monster fields,

though respected experts have estimated that the structure
could hold five to ten billion barrels of recoverable oil. However, with few completed wells, the reserves are not yet
regarded as proved. Moreover this is a relatively small part
of the general area which will be explored.

Finding the oil is only part of the problem. The oil must
then be removed from the ground, and only part of the oil is
economically recoverable. In recent years recovery has been
improving at an annual rate of about one-half of one percent.
This has been accomplished partly by injecting water back
into the well, thereby maintaining the pressures. If the rate
continues to improve, by 1980 it should be possible to recover 37.5 percent of the oil beneath the ground. According
to the Department of the Interior, that means that by 1980
an additional twenty-nine billion barrels will be added to the
nation's economically recoverable reserves even if no new discoveries are made.

However, the demand is expected to increase at a greater
rate, and unless new discoveries are made the reserves will
dwindle over the years. Experts predict that if new discoveries
are to be found in the United States they will lie mostly along
the continental shelf. The Atlantic coast contains sediments
that are similar to the Gulf coast, leading to speculations that
significant deposits may be found there. It has already been
demonstrated that the Pacific shelf is rich with oil.

The battle over the continental shelf will be fierce. It would
be the cheapest and easiest way to meet increases in the
domestic demand for petroleum without increasing imports.
Unfortunately, it is also the most hazardous to the environment.

Because of the tremendous growth in the demands for
energy in this nation, it is a virtual certainty that more oil
will have to be imported in the years ahead, regardless of who
wins the battle over the continental shelf.

One is forced to wonder why the continental shelf should be
sacrificed if in the long run the import quota system will have

to yield anyway. Why wait until the coastline has been destroyed before lifting the restrictions?

One other factor that should influence the nation's energy policies is the fact that man may abandon crude oil as a source of energy long before present reserves are exhausted. Much has been accomplished in recent years in the area of synthetic fuels, and there is sound indication that synthetics will replace crude oil in the years ahead. As the Library of Congress report suggested, new energy sources have crowded into the energy marketplace before existing sources were depleted in the past, and that trend will probably continue.

One of the world's greatest potential energy supplies lies beneath Colorado, in that state's oil-rich shale deposits. Shale contains an organic material known as kerogen. When the shale is heated to eight hundred to one thousand degrees, kerogen is transformed into a waxy oil that may then be refined into gasoline and other products.

Many experiments have been conducted in this area in the past, but at the present it is not economically rewarding. That undoubtedly will change in the years ahead with the development of improved technology. The concept is not new. Both Japan and Germany derived much of their oil during World War II from similar processes using coal and other substances.

There are many scientists who believe that there are numerous alternatives to petroleum as a source of energy. Dr. Howard A. Wilcox, a member of the Environmental Quality Advisory Board of the city of Santa Barbara, is one example. Wilcox is no idle dreamer. He was the project engineer on the Sidewinder missile program at the China Lake Naval Research Center in the California desert. Wilcox is a former Deputy Director of Defense for Research and Engineering in the Pentagon and a director of research and engineering for General Motors in Santa Barbara and Detroit. He is now an independent consultant.

During December 1970 Wilcox presented a research paper to an oil symposium at the University of California at Santa Barbara. In his paper, he raised this basic question:

"Do we really need to get the oil out from under the channel?"

He stated:

By now it is becoming generally understood that "recycling" is the basic technical concept in the fight for a clean environment. Man's "waste pile" is also his "resource pile." Relatively few atoms are being added to or subtracted from the earth at large. No material susbtance—even oil, for example —is fundamentally nonrenewable. Thus, when we burn gasoline or diesel fuel, we get mainly water plus oxides of carbon. But then we can use energy to weld the oxides of carbon and water back together into oil, if that be our need or our goal. In 1923 Fischer and Tropsch discovered a process which was suitable for the large-scale synthesis of gaseous, liquid, and solid hydrocarbon fuels and lubricants from water and the oxides of carbon. By 1938 this system was being used in six German plants for producing some four million barrels per year of gasoline, fuel oil, and various waxes. At that time an alternative and more efficient process, which had been discovered in 1913 by Bergius, supplanted the Fischer-Tropsch technique, and by 1944 twelve Bergius production plants in Germany were generating some two-tenths billion barrels per year of hydrocarbon products, mainly aviation gasoline. Since world consumption of petroleum was something over six billion barrels per year in the late 1950s, it seems clear to me that less than five hundred plants of the type the Germans were using in 1944 would have been able to meet the total world demand for hydrocarbon fuels and lubricants as of about ten years ago. The carbon compounds required for processing in such plants could come from freshly harvested vegetation, for example, or directly from airborne carbon dioxide. Since the total ultimate world reserves of petroleum were estimated as of 1960 to be less than 1750 billion barrels, I strongly suspect that in a few tens of decades we shall probably have to begin building large chemical plants to produce gaseous, liquid, and solid hydrocarbons on a large scale for our aircraft, land vehicles, ships, and other machinery.

Wilcox went on to describe another source of energy that is often scoffed at by other experts:

Let me now point out, however, that radiant energy from the sun can be practically pollution-free! It is showering in upon us whether we use it or not, so we might as well use it! In fact, the more efficiently we use it, the better, because it all eventually shows up as heat in the environment anyway!

The rate of flow of solar energy is so huge that in only three or four days it gives us an amount of energy equal to that stored in all the world's reserves of both petroleum and coal.

Solar activated photosynthesis is the process now responsible for producing all the food and other vegetation growing on earth, of course, yet on the average only three one-hundredths of 1 percent of all the solar energy reaching the surface of the earth is currently employed for photosynthesis. This average utilization efficiency is less than 1 percent of that achievable with high-yielding crops.

As mentioned earlier, land and marine vegetation can readily be used as the raw material from which to make aircraft, automotive, and diesel fuels. Hence, solar energy can easily be stored in copious quantities for use at night or during the dark stretches of winter.

In recognition of these facts, I think it might be prudent for us to leave most of our very limited reserves of high-grade fossil fuels in the ground for use only in case of severe emergency. We don't really need to get the oil out from under the Santa Barbara Channel! Likewise, even though nuclear energy production technologies should be vigorously researched and developed, in my view, I think nuclear fuels should probably be exploited only sparingly, for fission and fusion

energy will inevitably generate true thermal pollution, po-
tentially damaging radiation, various kinds of radioactive
wastes, and the continual danger of serious accidents.

Naturally, now, I can sense the swelling objections of the
opposition. They will probably say that the use of solar
energy is all very fine in principle, but that unfortunately it
is too expensive to be practical! This reminds me of the
statement one sometimes hears, that we're doomed to live in
filth because a high-quality environment is just too expensive
to be practical. These arguments are basically fallacious, I
feel, because they ignore the fundamentally cyclic or closed
character of our whole economic system. The profound truth
applicable here is that one man's dollar cost is always another
man's price, with his profit included! This means that the
making of a high-quality environment can become good business—profitable business—a "growth industry."

However, I hasten to point out that before big industry
can be caused to recycle its wastes in order to increase its
profits, we shall have to reshape our tax laws and our penalty
statutes in very far-reaching ways. The realities of economics
allow us the freedom, I believe, to redesign our system to a
very considerable extent, but it would be hopelessly idealistic
to ignore the fact that many serious difficulties will face
anyone who tries to change customary patterns.

As in the case of oil shale, the oil industry has consistently
sought to discredit possible sources of energy such as those
described by Wilcox. This is simply an attempt to protect
its own domain.

Most scientists believe that only shale that contains at least
twenty-five gallons of oil per ton will be attractive for commercial processing within the next few decades. But even with
that limitation the potential of Colorado's shale is profound.
The Department of the Interior indicated a few years ago that
there is more oil in shale deposits in the state of Colorado
alone than the entire world's proved reserves of crude oil. It is

inconceivable that the nation will choose to ignore such a valuable source of energy in the years ahead.

However, the attempt to develop this source will not be without its obstacles. Opposition will come from both the government and the oil industry, as it has in the past.

Nearly all oil-shale deposits in Colorado are owned by the federal government. Some lawmakers have attempted to block the exploitation of the shale in the belief that this great natural resource should be preserved for the future. Other legislators have followed the same course but for a different reason. They have served the oil industry's interest by trying to keep the shale from competing with present crude oil reserves.

In the past, the oil industry has dealt with the problem itself. In his book, *The Politics of Oil,* political scientist Robert Engler told of one such case.

According to Engler, in the 1950s Union Oil Company of California was conducting an extensive research program in Colorado, where the company owned shale deposits. The firm had planned to market shale-derived products on the West Coast, and in 1958 it announced that the goal had been achieved. But a short time later Union closed its Colorado operation. Why the change of heart? One reason may well have been the pressures brought against Union by other major oil companies.

At that time, America's largest oil companies had invested heavily in foreign operations, especially in the Middle East and Venezuela. They had hoped to import some of that oil into the United States. If Union had been successful in its Colorado program it would have jeopardized their plans. They did not know at the time that the federal government was about to impose its oil import quota system anyway.

In those days the nation's largest importer was the Gulf Oil Company. Gulf thus would have been severely crippled if Union's program had succeeded. But at that time Gulf held 120 million dollars of Union's convertible debentures. If Gulf had elected to exercise its option to convert the debentures to stock, it would have taken over control of Union. Gulf did not have to exercise that option. Union's Colorado program quietly came to an end.

There is one other facet to Colorado shale. This great source of energy destroys the myth that the oil import quota system is essential to national security. Theoretically, at least, the only thing stopping the exploitation of shale at the present time is cost. No one has come up with a means of extracting the oil from the shale cheaply enough to make it competitive with crude oil. However, during a time of national crisis, profits would not be the overriding motivation. Colorado shale could be converted into fuel to run the nation's implements of war regardless of the cost.

Again, one is forced to wonder. Why should the nation's coastline be sacrificed if there is an alternative?

The potential of oil shale is not well known. It is usually buried beneath the avalanche of propaganda from the oil industry and the federal government. However, exploitation of shale does pose hazards for the environment. Waste products from large-scale operations would leave mountains of useless by-products. If someone could dream up a plan for marketing the by-products, the problems of economics and waste disposal would be solved simultaneously, but so far no one seems to have the answer.

If anyone can solve that problem, it is probably the oil industry. One reason the industry has been so profitable over the years is that it has maximized the potential of its basic resource. But it was not always that way. Many years ago the industry used to burn natural gas just to get rid of it. But today the natural gas is about as important as the oil.

When it becomes economically advantageous to the industry to do so, it will undoubtedly apply that same caliber of ingenuity to solving the problems associated with the exploitation of shale.

This reluctance is not limited to the oil industry alone, of course. Any major industry follows a similar program. That may help explain why during the 1950s the role of nuclear power in the years ahead was consistently underestimated.

The Federal Power Commission now speculates that nuclear power will provide 40 percent of the nation's electricity by 1990, and as much as 60 percent by the year 2000. Those figures far exceed the expectations of a decade ago.

Today another source of electricity is in its infancy, and there are those who are saying it will never amount to much. No one knows whether the skeptics are right, because little is known about the "Devil's Caldron."

This fascinating story is unfolding in wide sectors of the world, most notably in Japan and Italy, but the United States is getting into the act rather late. It began in this country in the mid 1800s when William Bell "Grizzly" Elliott stumbled upon giant spouts of steam at Sulpher Creek, ninety miles north of San Francisco. The legendary mountain man was sure he had discovered the "Gates of Hell." What the old bear hunter had actually discovered were steam fumaroles generated by hot rocks several thousand feet below the surface of the earth. The area later became known as The Geysers, and it became a fashionable hot water spa for northern California. Although Elliott made his discovery in 1847, the Gates of Hell are still releasing giant vents of steam, and they are expected to do so for more than a thousand years.

But something new has been added since old man Elliott stumbled across the vents. The steam has been harnessed and is used today as fuel for the production of electricity. A Pacific Gas and Electric power plant that uses steam to turn its giant turbines produces enough electricity to take care of the demands of a considerable part of two counties. By 1975, PG&E hopes to expand the plant to generate as much as six hundred thousand kilowatts—enough electricity to meet the demands of a major city.

Scientists believe that Elliott's steam vents are a visual manifestation of a common phenomenon in many areas of the earth's twenty-mile-thick outer crust. Just as natural seeps once told wildcatters where to drill for oil, steam vents told modern-day explorers where to place their first North American geothermal power plant.

Here essentially is how it works. Molten rock, known as magma, is found in many areas of the earth's crust. At The Geysers, water is heated by the magma, converting it into superheated steam. The steam rises to the earth's surface through fissures. There is no limit to the amount of steam that can be generated as long as water is continually fed into the system. To harness the steam for domestic purposes, it is necessary to drill into the crust much the same as we now drill for oil. Some of the "steam wells" at The Geysers penetrate as deep as eight thousand feet. The steam is directed against the blades of the giant turbines just as nuclear generated steam, for instance, is used to turn the turbines of a nuclear power plant.

Scientists believe that in most cases there will be no serious by-products from natural steam. However, in some cases the steam may contain minerals that would be corrosive to metals and damaging to plant life. But even these problems can be overcome.

The procedure for drilling for steam is similar to that of drilling for oil, with a few variations. For example, drilling mud, which is used as a lubricant in drilling for oil, cannot be used in drilling for steam because the intense heat bakes it, and the mud becomes as hard as firebrick.

It is possible to have a blowout in drilling for steam, and no one knows that better than Union Oil Company of California. A subsidiary of Union operates the PG&E facility in northern California. In 1957, when one of the site's forty-two wells was being drilled, it blew out from a fault downhill from the well. According to Union Oil Company's official magazine, *Seventy Six* (September–October 1967), the drillers thought they had tapped a live volcano. The roar from the well could be heard for miles. Wild gusts of steam heaved up rocks and blew dirt all over the valley. Engineers calculated that the well belched up more than three thousand tons of rock and dirt. The volcanic storm toppled the drilling rig into the crater, where it disintegrated. Drillers tried vainly to seal the hole, but today it blows wild and free. Over the years it has been dubbed The Monster.

PG&E's facility is the first of its type in the United States. It is no accident that the plant was built on private property. Most areas that are conducive to geothermal operations are on federally owned property. For many years private corporations have tried to get the federal government to lease drilling rights for geothermal purposes, but the federal government has declined. The Department of the Interior has insisted that it was not authorized to award such leases. In 1966 Congress passed a bill authorizing the Interior Department to grant such leases, but the bill was vetoed by President Johnson.

There is wide disagreement over the role geothermal power will play in the future. According to the *Wall Street Journal* (December 10, 1970), Harrison Loesch, an assistant Interior Department secretary, told a Senate committee that "geothermal energy will at best supply only a small portion of the national power requirement in the future—probably less than 1 percent."

Federal Power Commission chairman John Nassikas later told the same committee, "This power source is presently viewed by geothermal experts as a possible rival to hydroelectric power and, in the long run, even nuclear power."

No one can say at this point just exactly how much of a role such things as shale and geothermal steam will play in the years ahead as this nation strives to meet a growing demand for energy. The only thing that can be said for certain is that, if either of these resources are to be realized, the thrust probably will have to come from within the oil industry. And as the situation now stands it would be against the industry's interest to exploit either resource.

It would be cheaper for the industry to continue the production of crude oil as long as there are enough reserves to supply a strong market. By the same token, if the industry succeeds in its current drive to monopolize all energy fuels, it

could only be expected to try to block development of geothermal power that would supplant its own fuels.

Thus it develops that there are alternatives; the nation's
energy problems are not impossible to solve; but this nation is
not presently inclined to solve them. The system works against
the American people by attempting to preserve the status quo.

There will come a day when in retrospect all of this will appear obvious.

But will that day come too late?

10

~~~~~~~~~~~~~~~~~~~~

Over the years the oil industry has been shaped into its present form by a variety of forces, some from within the industry and some from without. As a major industry operating under the free enterprise system, the primary objective of the oil industry has been to make money and to protect its domain, thus insuring that it will continue to make money in the years ahead. Few could argue with the morality of such goals. As conservative columnist William F. Buckley has argued, corporations are within their rights in trying to make an honest buck, but on dubious ethical grounds when they engage in other activities, such as underwriting philanthropic enterprises. If corporations have money to give away, Buckley argues, they should return it to their customers in the form of lower prices, not through benevolent contributions to local charities.

The profit motive is thus at the root of the oil industry's activities throughout the world, just as it is with any other private industry.

But the oil industry is in a relatively peculiar position. It has taken an active role in shaping legislation on the federal and state level, which has in turn shaped the industry itself. Although the industry has never been regarded fully as a public utility in this country, it is governed and protected by laws just as though it were. Perhaps this is not entirely wrong. The industry affects every person in this country in various ways. It should not be regarded simply as another business.

Over the years this concept has played a key role in the formation of the laws that affect the industry. The industry is what it is today because the laws governing its activities have helped shape it into its present form. It is clear that the industry must change if it is to serve the best interests of the people in the years ahead. And it is also clear that, if progress is to be made, the laws that have governed the industry in the past must be modified drastically. The basic motivation of the industry need not change. It should continue to be governed by a desire to earn money for its stockholders, but the means by which it achieves that end must be changed, and that can only be achieved by altering the forces that influence the industry.

Tax laws have played a special role in shaping the industry. Oil companies enjoy tax breaks that border on the ludicrous. Naturally, the industry has conducted its activities in such ways as to maximize the tax breaks. Any attempt to close these tax loopholes sends chills up the collective spines of oil executives throughout the land. They will fight bitterly to protect their realm, and it will take a brave U. S. Congress to change the rules of the game.

Of all the laws affecting the industry, none is more significant than the scandalous oil import quota system. The system set up the American people as a captive market. It has permitted the industry to engage in domestic operations at astronomical costs, and still sell its products at a profit. Without the import program, there would be no drilling off Santa Barbara, because it would not be economically rewarding.

The system limits imports east of the Rockies to 12.2 percent of domestic production within those states. The Department of the Interior restricts imports west of the Rockies to whatever is needed to make up the gap between domestic production and consumption.

The import quota system was established during the Presidency of Dwight D. Eisenhower, and it is this writer's opinion that the general was indeed motivated by a concern for national security. There are those who disagree. Sherman Adams, one of Eisenhower's top assistants, indicated in his memoirs of the Eisenhower Administration that economics, not national security, was the basis for the change.

"The imposing of import quotas on oil was primarily an economic decision brought about by an economic emergency, but the action . . . was based upon security considerations in accordance with the law. . . . Oil was coming into the United States from foreign fields at such a rate that the American oil-producing centers were being forced into desperate straits," Adams wrote.

The import program achieved one of its fundamental goals. It led to the development of a strong domestic oil industry— perhaps too strong. But it has contributed to one of the most shameful hoaxes ever perpetrated upon the American public. Reliable economists have estimated that the oil import quota system costs the American people at least 5.2 billion dollars a year in higher prices.

Bess Myerson, New York City Commissioner of Consumer Affairs, described the system during a Washington hearing as "The single most scandalous instance of exploitation which the American consumer must face in meeting her family's basic needs."

Experts have predicted that oil could be imported from the Middle East at a total cost of about $1.60 a barrel. That is about $1.90 a barrel cheaper than the price for domestic oil. Leaders of the industry have strongly denied the disparity in price. But they launched a bitter—and eventually successful —fight in 1967 and in 1970 when the federal government indicated it was considering abolishing the import system. If there is no great difference in price, why would the industry be so terrified over the prospects of a little competition?

Even if the need for import controls is legitimate, there is a better way to do it. It does not take a brilliant economist to realize that a tariff system would have accomplished the same goal—protecting the domestic oil industry—and would have at the same time fattened the U. S. Treasury. The Secretary of the Treasury in 1958 was Robert Anderson, a Texan. For some strange reason the government adopted a quota system instead of tariffs, and the price differential went into the pockets of the oil industry instead of the U. S. Treasury.

All of these things add up to a discouraging picture for the American consumer, who in the end pays for the whole charade. According to the New York *Times* Magazine (March 8, 1970), the average family of four in New York State pays an excess of a $102.32 a year for gasoline and heating oil. The same family would pay an extra $195.92 in Vermont or $258.00 in Wyoming.

The import system hurts the consumer in other ways as well. Fuel oil, which is high in sulphur content, is a serious air pollutant when used to generate electricity. The domestic industry does not produce enough low-sulphur oil to supply the numerous generating plants around the country that use oil for fuel. Low-sulphur fuel could be imported, but it is restricted under the system. As a result, many electric generating plants pollute the air, which could easily be minimized by importing low-sulphur fuel oil.

One of the most maddening aspects of the whole affair is that it would not be necessary to deal with any foreign oil companies if the country decided to import more oil. The oil would be purchased from American companies, which dominate the international oil industry. The nation imported approximately 20 percent of its oil in 1970. U.S. companies brought the oil into the country at foreign rates, sold it to its captive market at the domestic rate, and pocketed the difference.

There are a couple of legitimate problems in the importation of oil, even if the oil is purchased from domestic companies. Some of the money goes overseas, thus creating a drain on U.S. capital. In addition, the domestic industry employs thousands of persons, many of whom would lose their jobs if U.S.-based operations declined.

This could be minimized by replacing the import system with tariffs. The domestic industry could be protected and the tariffs could be used to subsidize research and development of alternative sources of energy.

The smokescreen of national security invariably clouds the picture. But the oil industry has admitted in the past, and it will admit again in the future when its needs are so served, that national security is not at stake. Production from domestic fields can be greatly increased if the need should arise. Sources of foreign oil are widespread, and it is inconceivable that all sources would be blocked at the same time. In addition, there are alternatives to oil, and they could be developed if the need arises.

The import quota system is merely a means of insuring the economic prosperity of the domestic oil industry at the cost of the consumer.

The oil import quota system has played a major role in shaping the modern oil industry, but that role is perhaps secondary to the complex tax structure under which the domestic industry thrives. The most disturbing of all the tax breaks enjoyed by the industry is the notorious oil depletion allowance.

In the early part of this century, oil men and others engaged in the exploitation of mineral resources began arguing that they deserved some sort of tax break because as they removed the resource from the ground they were, in effect, putting themselves out of business. In the original income tax law of 1913, a depletion deduction of up to 5 percent of gross income was permitted. The deduction was limited to the original cost of the property, or its market value in 1913. In 1918 the oil depletion allowance was pegged at 27½ percent of gross income up to a total of 50 percent of net income.

During the following years the allowance was challenged on many fronts. One of the men who helped preserve this special privilege was Andrew Mellon of Gulf Oil Company, who served as Secretary of the Treasury under three Presidents for a full decade (1921–31).

The reasoning behind the oil depletion allowance has mystified economists for years.

Former Jersey Standard president M. J. Rathbone once

justified the allowance "On the basis that when a prospector found an oil field and produced that oil field, he was in effect going out of business." But other businessmen see profits derived from oil production as business income, pure and simple.

The oil depletion allowance is one reason why some major oil companies have succeeded in paying only minimal taxes.

In 1969, for the first time in more than four decades, the U. S. Congress reduced the allowance, from 27½ percent to 22 percent. However, the allowance for oil shale was maintained at 15 percent, which may help explain why the oil industry would prefer to deal in crude oil as opposed to shale.

Even at 22 percent, the allowance gives the oil industry a tremendous loophole. There is no reason to expect the industry to try to develop alternative forms of fuel if such a program would cost the industry the oil depletion allowance. Why, for example, should the industry be expected to develop solar energy if there is no chance that it can claim it is depleting the sun, and thus eligible for another depletion allowance?

The oil depletion allowance is one of the principle forces that have made the industry what it is today. It must be revised further if the industry is to change.

All of this is fairly easy to understand. Any businessman would sympathize with an industry that is trying to protect its own interests and guarantee its future. But it is harder to forgive the gross abuse of power and wealth that continues to typify the oil industry even today.

Standard Oil Company of Ohio was charged by the federal government in September 1970 with fixing prices at arbitrarily high levels on gasoline and other products sold under its Sohio label. The federal suit accused the company of conspiring through secret agreements to set prices charged for Sohio products by service stations not owned by the company. As a result of the alleged price fixing, the suit charged, "Customers have been deprived of the opportunity of purchasing petroleum products, TBA [tires, batteries, and automotive assessories] products and service works in a free and competitive market." The suit also said that service station managers "have been deprived of their rights to determine their own sales prices on the products and services they will offer."

In other cases, federal enforcement agencies have charged individual oil companies with deliberately trying to mislead the public. Ironically, some of these cases accuse the great polluters of falsely portraying themselves as conscientious custodians of a clean environment.

Standard Oil Company of California, which is one of the largest oil companies in the world, was involved in one such case in the summer of 1970. Standard came out with an additive that was sold in gasoline marketed by its Chevron stations, called F-310. The company hired former astronaut and erstwhile aquanaut Scott Carpenter to appear in television commercials plugging the product. In one typical commercial Carpenter was shown standing in front of a building with a huge sign reading "Chevron Research Center." As it turned out, the "research center" was the Riverside County Courthouse in the desert community of Palm Springs. Carpenter's pitch went like this:

"I'm Scott Carpenter. We're attaching a clear balloon to this car to show you one of the most meaningful gasoline achievements in history. The balloon is filling with dirty exhaust emissions that go into the air and waste mileage.

"Now Standard Oil of California has accomplished the development of a remarkable gasoline additive, Formula F-310, that reduces exhaust emissions from dirty engines. The same car [shown with a clear balloon], after just six tanksful of Chevron with F-310; no dirty smoke, cleaner air. A major breakthrough to help solve one of today's critical problems. And since dirty exhaust is wasted gasoline, F-310 keeps good mileage from going up in smoke. Cleaner air, better mileage—Chevron with F-310 turned dirty smoke into good, clean mileage. There isn't a car on the road that shouldn't be using it."

A balloon attached to the car in the second sequence appeared to be full of just good clean air, contrasting sharply with the black balloon shown in the first part of the commercial. Californians who understood what it takes to make smog were immediately suspicious of the advertisement. No car emits "smog" directly from its exhaust pipe. Instead, it emits various pollutants, such as oxides of nitrogen, which must be acted upon by the sun's rays in order to produce the yellowish eye-irritant known as "smog."

The California Air Resources Board conducted a survey of more than eight hundred cars using various brands of gasoline. The board issued a report stating there was no significant cutback in pollution emissions when cars used Chevron gasoline with F-310. The People's Lobby, an anti-pollution organization, took the case before the Federal Trade Commission. The FTC conducted an extensive investigation and charged the company with false advertising. The balloon commercials, for example, were deceptive, the agency charged. The FTC said the car that inflated the black balloon used "a specially formulated gasoline" that dirtied the engine and produced a black exhaust. Conversely, the clear balloon that was supposedly inflated by the clean exhaust of the F-310 vehicle had "large amounts of pollutants."

The FTC said that "using Chevron with F-310 will not significantly reduce air pollution generally, or air pollution caused by motor vehicles or automobile emissions of carbon monoxide and hydrocarbons."

Standard decided to fight the charges. It filed an appeal in the federal courts, and immediately embarked on an even more aggressive advertising campaign. Full- and double-page advertisements were taken out in more than thirty newspapers throughout the state of California, and a saturation advertising campaign was conducted on television, with Scott Carpenter at the helm.

The oil industry is not a passive participant in the events that directly influence our lives. In all too many cases the industry puts its own interests first, and uses its power and its wealth to harm the public. This is especially true when the oil industry's interests are closely aligned with other powerful groups, such as the automotive industry and the insurance companies. This was demonstrated most clearly in California during the general election in November 1970. For many years the people of California have struggled unsuccessfully with the problem of mass transit. Los Angeles, for example, unlike other cities of that size in wide sectors of the country, is virtually without a mass transit system. As a result, the automobile is king in Southern California, and private passenger cars have emerged as the No. 1 source of air pollution. The city's freeways are overcrowded. Vast reaches of the Southern California landscape have been blacktopped to serve the needs of the auto-oriented society.

Most of these problems could be resolved through the development of a good rapid transit system. However, due to the sprawling nature of the Los Angeles area, it will be extremely expensive to develop such a system at this late date. But regardless of cost, it has to be done sometime, and the longer Californians wait the more expensive it will become. Realizing this, a number of proposals have been put forth in recent years to help alleviate the problem. But the insurmountable barrier in all cases has been money.

In 1970, a Democratic state senator from San Diego, James R. Mills, came up with a novel approach to the problem. State taxes on gasoline were earmarked for highways, and could be used for no other purpose. Mills, an ardent conservationist, realized California could not go on indefinitely paving its landscape. He drafted a proposal that would have allowed counties to divert up to one-fourth of their highway taxes for mass transit and for air pollution control. The California state legislature quickly approved the measure for the general election, and it was placed on the November ballot.

The measure, called Proposition 18, won immediate, widespread support. In an editorial, the Los Angeles *Times* called it the most important measure on the statewide ballot.

California voters also reacted favorably to the idea. Mervin Field, director of the California Poll, historically one of the most accurate public opinion polls in the state, reported about two weeks prior to the election that more than half of the voters favored the proposition.

But as the election entered the eleventh hour, the state was inundated by a massive, distorted advertising campaign. The campaign was based upon scare tactics. It accused the proposition of being a "tax hoax." Voters were warned in the massive campaign that a vote for Proposition 18 would be a vote for higher taxes.

The charge was a myth.

Less than a week prior to the election, four elderly Californians who suffered from emphysema and tuberculosis joined with the Sierra Club in a law suit seeking an injunction against the fradulent election campaign. The suit named, among others, four oil companies: California Standard, Union, Shell, and Texaco.

The suit charged:

> The deceptive and misleading statement that taxes will automatically go up if the proposition is passed is blanketing the state via saturation campaign in the media. For example, in the Los Angeles area, the NBC affiliate [KNBC-TV] has orders placed for ten spots opposing Proposition 18—a total of six thousand dollars' worth of ads to be run by the station between today and election day [then four days away]. The NBC affiliate in San Francisco [KRON-TV] has been paid to run twenty spot announcements in opposition to Proposition 18 in the next four days.
>
> In addition to the massive radio and television campaign sponsored by the oil companies and their committee, their false and fraudulent message is presently spread on some five hundred billboards throughout California.

In support of the suit, Mills submitted the following affidavit:

I, State Senator James R. Mills (D-San Diego), declare as follows:

I am the author of Proposition 18, which both Houses of the Legislature authorized to go before the California voters at the November 1970 election.

The opponents of Proposition 18, primarily financed by the highway special interests, have disseminated a major misrepresentation about what Proposition 18 says and what it would provide.

The opponents of Proposition 18 contend Proposition 18 is supposed to raise taxes. Proposition 18, in fact, does nothing of the sort. It is not a revenue measure; it raises no new taxes; it only removes a restriction in the State Constitution which has required gasoline tax revenues be expended only for highway construction and maintenance. Proposition 18 would authorize the use of revenues from motor vehicle fuel tax and license fees for control of environmental pollution caused by motor vehicles, and for public transportation, including mass transit systems, upon approval by the electorate of such areas affected. Such expenditures would be limited to 25 percent of the revenues generated in each area. Proposition 18, in other words, would allow for the real location of present revenues, not the raising of new ones.

In my experience as a State Senator, the well-financed highway interests have been frequently guilty of making misleading and even false statements. The last-minute campaign against Proposition 18 is yet the latest example of this pattern of misrepresentation.

In the past three days, TV and radio stations have begun to carry numerous advertisements against Proposition 18—all containing the above-mentioned misrepresentation about Proposition 18. Because the misrepresentation is made at the last moment before the election, it is difficult, if not impossible to answer—at least by counteradvertisements which would be placed by the proponents of Proposition 18. The plain fact is that we who favor Proposition 18 can't prepare radio spots, contact radio stations, and place rebuttals on the air before the November 3rd election—there is just not enough time. It is my opinion, therefore, that the only means of correcting the misrepresentation perpetrated is for a court to order that these misleading advertisements be immediately withdrawn from the air.

The office of the Legislative Council, the official legal adviser to the state legislature, submitted an opinion stating:

"It is our opinion that, if the people approve and ratify Proposition 18, it would not, as a matter of law, require any increase in highway users taxes."

It was a lesson in futility. A random survey conducted on October 29 revealed that an overwhelming number of voters were influenced by the advertising. According to the suit, "A research team showed sixty-six (66) randomly selected interviewees a photograph of the billboard advertisement. Forty-seven (47) of the sixty-six (66) responded that Proposition 18 'automatically raises my taxes.' Only five (5) indentified the measure as one to improve rapid transit. The others answered 'don't know.'"

As election day approached, pollster Field reported on a San Francisco television station that among voters who had seen or heard no advertisements concerning Proposition 18, four out of five indicated they would vote yes on 18 after they were shown a copy of the proposition. The odds dropped at least 25 percent among those who had seen the misleading advertisements. Field concluded that the advertising campaign had a substantial effect.

Proposition 18 was defeated by a 54 percent to 46 percent vote.

When it was all over, the discouraging defeat emerged as a lesson in modern power politics. Campaign statements filed in the state capital of Sacramento told the story. Opponents to Proposition 18 spent $333,455.69 to get the measure defeated. Backers of the measure spent a pitiful $15,275.20.

Where did the money come from? Four of the donations were anonymous, but later were traced to Mobil Oil Company (thirty thousand dollars), Standard Oil Company of California (forty-five thousand dollars), and Gulf Oil Corporation (twenty thousand dollars). California Standard was listed in the campaign statement as contributing thirty thousand dollars, so its total contribution was actually seventy-five thousand dollars.

Other donors included Shell Oil Company, fifty thousand dollars; Union Oil Company, twenty thousand dollars; Texaco, twenty thousand dollars; Phillips Oil, fifteen thousand dollars; Humble Oil, twelve thousand dollars; Standard Oil of Indiana, five thousand dollars; Getty Oil, five thousand dollars; Douglas Oil, five thousand dollars; Sun Oil, two thousand dollars; and Marathon Oil, one thousand dollars. The Southern California Automobile Club was listed as contributing twelve thousand dollars, and the California State Automobile Association kicked in another ten thousand dollars.

On the other side of the ledger, Kaiser Industries, which includes a chain of hospitals, was the biggest individual donor, with twenty-five hundred dollars. Others included the Tuberculosis and Respiratory Disease Association of California, five hundred dollars; the Sierra Club, one hundred dollars; and the League of Women Voters, one hundred dollars.

The opponents outspent the backers twenty-two to one.

Why were the oil companies willing to give so much? A mass transit system would have meant fewer cars on the roads, and that would have meant lower profits. It also would have meant fewer traffic deaths, cleaner air, and a better life for the people of California.

But in power politics those things do not matter.

11

In December 1970, nearly two years after the Santa Barbara oil spill, a bureaucratic scientist traveled from Washington to Santa Barbara with a message for the residents of that city by the sea. A few years earlier, Dr. William T. Pecora had considered taking a job with the University of California at Santa Barbara. But he decided instead to stay with the U. S. Geological Survey, and a short time later he became the Director of the agency. Pecora had but a single mission in his trip west in December 1970. His assignment was to tell the people of Santa Barbara that they had lost their fight to save the channel from further exploitation by the oil industry.

While in Santa Barbara he appeared before numerous clubs and luncheons. In each case he gave basically the same off-the-cuff talk. He told the people to "face the facts." The battle for the channel was over.

One of his last appearances was before an oil symposium at the university. About four hundred persons were attending the symposium. One of those in the audience was Thomas D. Barrow, president of Humble Oil. Humble was the big winner in the channel lease sale of 1968, and it thus had a greater stake in the channel than any other oil company.

Standing before the crowd, Pecora again warned Santa Barbara to face the facts. Finally, as if to make his message painfully clear, Pecora said:

"I don't personally give a damn whether there is drilling [in the channel] or not."

Just so there would be no misunderstanding, a few minutes later he repeated the statement.

The following day the symposium concluded. One of the last speakers was Commander William E. Lehr, Jr., Chief of the Pollution Control Branch in the office of Research and Development at Coast Guard Headquarters in Washington, D.C. Lehr told the symposium that there had been no major breakthroughs in the effort to develop the tools to contain and remove massive oil spills. In effect, he said that if another blowout occurred that day in the Santa Barbara Channel the oil industry would not be much better equipped than it had been two years earlier. Lehr's observations offered a shocking sequel to Pecora's pronouncements a day earlier. The oil industry had won in the fight for the Santa Barbara Channel, but everybody knew it was a tainted victory. Pecora had admitted as much the day before when he told the symposium, "You are going to have pollution here—face it."

It had rained heavily during the three-day symposium. From time to time the rain had stopped and the sun melted away the clouds, bathing Santa Barbara in warm sunlight. The mountains behind the city, covered with the green grass brought by the first rains, towered over the community as majestically as ever. Offshore, the Channel Islands contrasted sharply with the blue water and the clearing horizon. Nine offshore platforms marred the picture, but few would have denied that Santa Barbara still ranked as one of the world's most beautiful communities.

What had it all come to?

The channel was still there, nearly as beautiful as ever. Scores of experts had examined the waters repeatedly and concluded that the 1969 oil spill had not been an ecological disaster. Fish continued to thrive in the channel, and the area appeared to have recovered fully.

But Santa Barbara would never be the same again, and it is that unwanted change that stands today as a monumental disaster.

Dr. Gordon J. F. MacDonald, of Santa Barbara, a member of the President's Council on Environmental Quality, said it as well as anyone.

"The risk of oil pollution can be minimized," MacDonald said. "But there is a greater risk that the basic quality of life in the Santa Barbara area will be changed. If it is dominated by oil, it will be a different Santa Barbara."

It is this domination that will pose the greatest threat to Santa Barbara, and to many areas along the nation's coastline, during the years ahead. It does not take a marine biologist to realize that if the offshore areas are transformed into industrial districts the sea and the adjacent coastline will be altered dramatically.

Nowhere is this more apparent than along the Gulf Coast, which has a long history of offshore operations by the minerals industry. Oil production began off the coast of Louisiana in the 1920s and reached major proportions in the fifties and sixties. As of 1970 there were 1792 platforms off the Louisiana and Texas coasts. The Louisiana Department of Conservation has estimated that more than twenty-five thousand wells have been drilled off the state's shoreline. This does not include hundreds of dry holes.

The wells are connected by a massive network of underwater pipelines. In many areas the topography has been reshaped to accommodate the needs of the industry.

As a result a major battle has developed between the oil and fishing industries over the use of the Gulf Coast. Although oil pollution has not significantly reduced the number of fish, the industrial nature of the offshore area has limited its value for commercial fishing. The platforms and a wide range of underwater equipment have posed such a threat to commercial fishing rigs that many of the fishermen have been forced to go elsewhere.

The same area is world-renowned for its high production of oysters, shrimp, fish, fur, and waterfowl. According to Lyle S. St. Amant of the Louisiana Wild Life and Fisheries Commission, Louisiana produces between eight hundred million and 1.2 billion pounds of commercial fish annually, or more than 20 percent of the total U.S. production. That does not include recreational fishing. The commercial fishery of Louisiana is valued at 150 million dollars annually, plus recreational fishing and tourism. The area also supports fur production, which in peak years exceeded the combined production of all the other forty-seven conterminous states. From five to seven million waterfowl spend their winters there.

In a paper presented during the Santa Barbara oil symposium, St. Amant minimized the damage from single, spectacular cases of oil pollution. Instead, he placed greater emphasis upon possible accumulative effects of continued pollution on a minor scale, and damage to the area brought on by the industrial activities along the shoreline and off the coast.

In his paper, St. Amant stated:

"Possibly between thirty thousand and forty thousand or more separate operations may have occured [offshore], each of which caused some disruption of the local ecology and no doubt resulted in localized pollution which lasted for various lengths of time."

He went on to say:

"At this point in time, it is difficult to predict the future except to point out that there must be a breaking point in the equilibrium of the ecosystem and none of us know how near we are to it. Fishery statistics indicate little change in the productivity of the Louisiana coast over the past thirty years, but one does not have to be a professional ecologist to realize that this type of environmental abuse cannot continue forever. On the other hand, the occurrences on Louisiana's coast demonstrate the apparent resilience and buffered nature of marine ecosystems and gives some idea of the amount of abuse that such areas can withstand. If nothing else, these areas should be studied in as much detail as possible to determine the mechanics of the system. They also should serve as an example of what may be in store for other coastal areas if a national coastal management sys-

tem is not developed soon and if priorities and standards
are not set for mulitiple-use programs."

What especially troubled St. Amant is the possibility that
offshore operations may be contributing small amounts of
toxic elements to the environment that in the long run will
have a more devastating effect than a singular catastrophic
incident. In other words, the situation may be far worse than it
appears. He put it this way:

"Certainly the significance of the continual addition to and
accumulative effect of sublethal pollutants on the environment is probably the most important ecological question facing
us today. While this question remains unanswered, environmental management decisions based only on our present
knowledge of short-term gross effects of pollution and/or
environmental manipulation may eventually prove to be disastrous."

How many years did it take for man to realize the danger
of mercury pollution? For years scientists thought mercury
would collect harmlessly on the floor of the ocean. Only recently have we realized that mercury does not behave the way
we expected it to, and it now poses a terrifying threat to our
well-being.

Offshore operations may also weaken the area's resistance
to threats not directly associated with oil. For example, St.
Amant cited a drop in oyster production in Louisiana from
a high of 1,290,000 barrels annually in 1942 to seven hundred thousand barrels in 1944. The reduced rate of production
continued for several years.

"This occurred at a time of maximum and largely uncontrolled oil pollution and resulted in litigation between the
oyster and oil industries," St. Amant wrote. "Considerable research developed because of this litigation. A research unit
from Texas A&M University did extensive research for the
petroleum industry during the mid- and late forties and considerable research was also contracted by the Louisiana Wild
Life and Fisheries Commission. Results of this research indicated that the heavy oyster mortalities were caused by the

fungus *Dermacystidium marinum* and not by oil. It was never made clear, however, why *D. marinum* suddenly reached epidemic proportions in the 1940s when it was demonstrated to be endemic in the oyster population from oysters preserved in the 1920s. Since *D. marinum* is more prevalent in areas of high salinity and high temperatures, salt water intrusion [into the oyster beds] resulting from navigation and pipeline canals associated with the oil industry may have been a major cause of the oyster losses, though oil per se did not prove to be excessively toxic."

It appears that we really do not know what we are doing—in the Gulf as well as elsewhere—but we are proceeding full speed ahead anyway.

We may be heading for disaster due partly to the nation's failure to establish a comprehensive oceanographic research program. Not too many years ago there was much talk about the sea, about its future, and about how little we knew about it. Great plans were laid for research. Numerous governmental agencies and private industries pledged financial support to the growing field of marine science.

But the nation chose instead to concentrate on the more glamorous conquest of space. Billions of dollars were poured into the space program, with the result that America was indeed the victor in the race for the moon.

Meanwhile we did little to learn about the ocean. The ambitious research programs were put on the shelf as more and more dollars were diverted into the space program and other projects of the late sixties. The result has been the present absurd predicament; we know more about outer space than we know about our own seas. It is absurd because man was not likely to venture into space unprepared, but we have readily demonstrated that man can indeed stumble into the ocean unprepared.

What sense does it make to tiptoe into space, and then stomp into the sea?

There is a profound need to slacken our pace in the exploitation of the sea, and to speed up our research into that little-known realm of deep silence.

There are a number of ways this could be done, all of which would take money. But the money is available. Consumers in this nation are subsidizing the domestic oil industry through the scandalous oil import quota system. But at this late date it would be disastrous to the industry, and to the thousands who depend upon it for employment, to suddenly scratch the import program. It would make far more sense to replace the import program with a tariff system. The tariffs could be used to help us learn more about the sea, and to develop alternative sources of energy.

The fight over the continental shelf is more than simply a dispute over how the coastline should be used. The fight is the result of a major contradiction in philosophies.

During the Santa Barbara oil symposium, Professor R. W. Nash of the university's history department dealt briefly with this contradiction. Quoting from the writings of the nineteenth-century economist and philosopher, Henry George, Nash posed the question: "How can we have both progress and poverty?"

"We have only to recast 'poverty' in aesthetic and spiritual terms to see the point," Nash said. "Thus we could ask how is it that we continue to progress in terms of quantity, energy, Gross National Product, and the so-called standards of living and yet find that many Americans (even rich ones) experience an increasingly 'poorer' life. We are poorer, I submit, in the satisfactions of living. The quality of life we lead amidst a trillion-dollar GNP is declining. For instance, we find ourselves with marvelous automobiles and nowhere worth driving to. We have lavish picture-windows in our homes, in Pasadena, for instance, and nothing to see but smog. We have the best diet of any people in history but in the Los Angeles basin air pollution prevents schoolchildren from exercising on roughly half the days, and the UCLA football team has to practice at 5 A.M. before the smog alert. That's what I mean by progress and poverty.

"My thesis today is that oil development in the Santa Barbara Channel is an example of progress and poverty. The more development we have, I would argue, the poorer we become. So I am prepared to say 'No' to oil. Not 'No, unless technology improves' or 'No, until oil is needed next century' or 'No, if more than a dozen platforms' but just plain 'No.' Of course this is an extreme statement; of course it's uncompromising. But I feel the time has come for extreme statements and uncompromising stands. In fact I reject the whole notion of compromise that government-blessed oil producers present to us. It is as if a man came to your front door and declared it his intention to rape your wife. You protest. 'All right,' he replies, 'let's compromise. I'll only rape her for ten minutes.' Oil developers in the Channel are making the same kind of deal with their sanctuaries and buffer zones and improved technology argument. To continue the previous metaphor, this is like saying 'Well, we won't rape all of her' or 'We'll use great technique in executing the rape—she'll love it.' The point is that the husband and wife, or the community of Santa Barbara, loses inevitably in this so-called compromise. The oil industry is not giving us anything that the Creator did not put here in the first place. It's a heads they win, tails we lose arrangement. Let's never forget that the whole Santa Barbara Channel was a "sanctuary" before the first rig. Those who liked it that way lose with every step toward development."

The Santa Barbara controversy is more than a dispute over natural resources. It is more than a disagreement over the possibilities of pollution. More than anything else, Santa Barbara's loss demonstrates a crisis in national priorities and leadership. It is also a profound example of why many young people today are unable to communicate with their elders.

During the oil symposium of 1970, Humble's president, Thomas Barrow, insisted repeatedly that the only alternative to drilling in the channel and along the continental shelf was to lower the standard of living in the United States.

His statement was false, and Barrow knew it. There are many alternatives to drilling on the continental shelf, and the lowering of the standard of living need not be one of them.

Barrow's concern was economic, pure and simple. His company had invested heavily in the channel, and Humble stood to gain much through the exploitation of its leases.

The oil industry tried desperately to cloud the issue, but those who followed it closely saw through the subterfuge. Unfortunately, the government joined with the oil industry in trying to cover up the motives behind the drilling, and it consistently served the needs of the industry more than it served the people.

For example, during the symposium the question of increasing imports as one means of ending offshore drilling came up. Dr. Pecora rose to the challenge and mentioned that if imports were increased, more oil would enter the country by tanker. He then read from a list of history's ten greatest spills, of which nine were caused by tankers. The largest was the *Torrey Canyon* incident, which dumped seven hundred thousand barrels of crude oil into the sea off Lands End, England. Pecora left the impression that tankers pose the greatest threat of oil pollution, and the environmentalists would be defeating their own purpose if they succeeded in substituting imports for offshore drilling. But Pecora knew as well as anyone that offshore production would not reduce the need for tankers appreciably. Most of the oil produced offshore will eventually have to be moved somewhere else anyway, and in most cases it will be moved by tankers. Thus offshore production actually increases the chance of pollution by tanker. Is it possible that such an obvious fact merely slipped Pecora's mind?

There is also a considerable possibility that far more oil could be piped into the United States from Canada if import restrictions were dropped. Much of Canada has yet to be explored, and a ready market to the south would surely stimulate exploration and discovery.

It is not essential to produce oil from the Santa Barbara

Channel, or from anywhere else along the continental shelf. All drilling in the coastal waters along the United States should be halted immediately. No more leases should be sold. The ocean should be preserved for those who will come this way long after we have passed from the picture.

Santa Barbara launched this nation on an irreversible drive toward guaranteeing a cleaner environment for every American. More progress has been made in that direction since the blowout at Platform A than in the entire history of the United States. The blowout was one of the things that shocked the U. S. Congress into passing the National Environmental Policy Act, regarded by many conservationists as the most important single piece of environmental legislation ever passed by the federal legislature.

The Act requires all federal agencies to submit reports to the Council on Environmental Quality on projects that may have an impact on the environment. The Council was established by the Act. According to Dr. MacDonald, one of three members of the Council, the Act "revolutionized" the way the federal government does business. However, one year after the Council was created, its budget was cut by one-third. Its staff numbers a grand total of fourteen.

Through the Council on Environmental Quality, for the first time this country has the means to formulate and maintain a nationwide policy on environmental control.

Santa Barbara did more than its share to give the nation this valuable tool. In the years ahead, this country and indeed the world will face a continuing challenge as it strives to correct the mistakes of the past and reduce the errors of the future.

One of the things at stake is the sea itself.

People tend to think of the ocean as an unlimited expanse of self-cleansing water, and it is hard to imagine poisoning the entire ocean. But not too many years ago, people were saying the same thing about the Mississippi River. It was impossible to believe that man could seriously endanger the original Ol' Man River. But the fate of the river was told graphically in the June 1969 issue of *Conservation Now,* published by the San Fernando Valley Group, Angeles Chapter, Sierra Club:

> The once-beautiful Mississippi is now referred to by some as "the colon of mid-America."
>
> In the fall of 1966 a group of conservationists inspected the Mississippi by boat in the vicinity of St. Louis and were shocked to see more than 100 pipes pouring untreated sewage directly into the Mississippi.
>
> Water samples taken from the river below St. Louis were found to be so toxic that even when diluted *ten times* with clear water, fish placed in the mixture died in less than one minute! When the samples were diluted 100 times, the test fish still perished within 24 hours. Fortunately, the people living south of St. Louis have more rugged constitutions than do fish.
>
> Congressman John Blatnik of Minnesota was shocked by the condition of the river: "The Mississippi is already bad by the time it reaches Minneapolis . . . by the time it gets down to Iowa . . . it is getting quite serious, and south of that, by the time all the petrochemicals and other industrial oils, chemicals and slaughterhouse wastes along the way are dumped into it—from St. Louis on, it is impossible."
>
> "From that point southward," Blatnik continued, "the Mississippi is so bad that state health departments, and the Federal Public Health Service have posted signs forbidding people even to eat lunch along its banks, let alone go wading, swimming or water skiing. The concentration of infectious bacteria in just the spray from the river, when deposited on a person's face or lips, can cause typhoid, colitis, hepatitis, diarrhea, or infections in the bloodstream.
>
> "In fact," said Blatnik, "in plain, simple but honest language, it is rapidly becoming an open, running sewer."

It is not inconceivable that a similar fate awaits the oceans, vast though they may be.

Famed undersea explorer Jacques Cousteau paused briefly in Monte Carlo in 1970 at the end of a three-year, seven-month expedition around the world. That great lover of the sea summed up his findings in one sentence:

"The ocean is dying."

An Epilogue

Several months before the general election, in May 1970, California's then deputy attorney general, Charles O'Brien, sat in his Los Angeles office talking with this writer, who was on assignment for the Los Angeles *Times*. O'Brien, a seasoned lawyer who had been instrumental in getting some of California's most effective law-enforcement legislation through the state legislature, was discussing a growing trend among Americans to arm themselves out of fear.

After the interview, the conversation turned casually to politics. California's longtime attorney general, Tom Lynch, had announced plans to retire, and O'Brien had decided to run for the top post. As Lynch's chief deputy, O'Brien knew the duties of the office well, and he felt qualified to succeed Lynch. But he was a political novice.

"How is the campaign going?" he was asked.

"About as well as could be expected," O'Brien said. And then he swiveled his chair around and gazed for a long moment out the window of the state building. Finally, he turned and leaned across the desk.

"But politics . . ." he said slowly, shaking his head. "Politics . . . this business of running for office . . . is a terrible thing."

Charlie O'Brien lost by a narrow margin. Fortunately for California, his opponent, Evelle Younger, then district attorney of Los Angeles County, was also qualified to become the state's top legal officer.

When it was all over, O'Brien was asked what he planned to do next.

"Well," he said. "I'm going fishing. And then I'm going to look for a job."

There are other Charlie O'Briens in this country. They enter politics briefly, learn a little about themselves and a lot about the system, and are rarely seen in the political arena again. Why?

CBS's anchorman Walter Cronkite, one of the most experienced political reporters in the nation, answered that question as well as anyone in an interview in *Look* magazine (November 17, 1970).

"I could see myself in politics," Cronkite said. "I think it would be marvelous to be in the United States Senate. I would like it. But I wouldn't like to go through what you have to go through in order to get there."

And therein lies one of the great weaknesses of the American political system. America does not always send her best people into positions of power; instead, she often sends those who are best able—and willing—to adapt themselves to that special brand of self-torture called The Campaign.

America suffers from a grave crisis in leadership. The winners in the voting booth are usually those who are able to project the best image at a time when weary people are thirsting for simple answers to complex problems.

In all too many cases, the instant answers of thirty-second television commercials have robbed us of depth and given us instead a plastic victor. Why must this be so? The answer casts dark shadows over the present system, and it helps explain why the American people have been largely unsuccessful in their efforts to make their government more responsive to such things as the deteriorating environment.

At the root of the problem is the campaign itself. Shortly after Ronald Reagan announced that he would try to unseat Edmund G. Brown as the governor of California in 1966, I interviewed the former movie actor in a northern California city. Reagan, who had never held public office, had decided to launch his political career by taking a stab at one of the most important offices in the nation—that of governor of the nation's most populous state. His campaign was only a few weeks old at that time, but the race for the governor's mansion was well under way.

He talked for a while about the issues, and I was impressed with his sincerity, although not always with his answers. Finally, the talk turned to the campaign itself.

"You know, I've been in the motion picture business for most of my life," he said. "I knew before I got into politics what it was like to be knifed. But I will tell you one thing, never in all of my life have I ever been involved in anything as vile and as vicious as politics."

Reagan, who was clearly shocked at the time, learned to live with it. But in those early days, when he was nothing more than the prince of the Late Show who wanted to be the governor of California, he was deeply troubled by the reality of politics.

Most political campaigns last at least a year, including both the primary and the general election. That amounts to at least twelve months of slurs and counterslurs; distortions and lies; personal animosities that keep honest men awake at night; quick answers that will get votes, but not necessarily solve the problems; promises that can never be fulfilled.

A year like that can change a man.

Campaigns are as expensive as they are misleading. It takes a staggering sum to win high public office in this nation today, especially if the campaign must be conducted in heavily populated areas where communications media abound. It is not uncommon for a political candidate to spend well over one million dollars to win a seat in the United States Senate, for example. The money rarely comes from the candidate himself.

Where does the money come from? It does not come from little old ladies who give ten dollars each out of their pensions because they want to see an honest man in government.

It usually comes in huge sums from people who expect to earn a good return on their investment.

Thus the victor goes into office with scores of silent partners following a long campaign in which he learned the meaning of compromise. He is a winner, but he knows that two, four, or six years later, it will start all over again. So he listens when his silent partners speak.

These are the men who must make the decisions upon which the future of man will depend. They will be difficult decisions. As was the case in Santa Barbara, the stakes will be staggering, and the pressures will be enormous.

There will be a profound tendency to clamp down on the little guy, while the big offenders escape unscathed. In short, we may clobber the mice for nibbling at the cheese but let the fat cats steal the whole banquet.

For about sixty million years the fierce saber-toothed tiger reigned as king of the North American continent. He survived because he adapted to his environment. Yet in a span of less than four thousand years man may well have moved closer to extinction because he has tried to make his environment adapt to him.

The saber-toothed tiger lost. Man, too, is not indestructible.

Survival will depend upon making the right decisions at the right time.

Can we do it?

INDEX

D